THE INTIMATE FAMILY

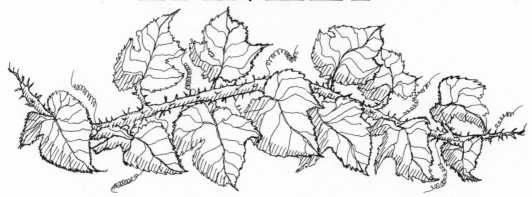

Hope for Hurried Homes

by Marlee Alex

Illustrations by Diane Hubbard Bailey

QUESTAR PUBLISHERS, INC.

Sisters, Oregon

THE INTIMATE FAMILY

ISBN 0-945564-26-0

This Family Workbook
belongs to

_____

_____

_____

_____

_____
PARENTS' & CHILDREN'S SIGNATURES

_____

_____
HOME ADDRESS

_____
HOME TELEPHONE NUMBER

Our written entries in this book were begun _____
                                                        DATE

and were concluded _____
                              DATE

We dedicate our commitment in family living to

_____

contents

Renewing Our Purpose & Vision

Preparing for New Horizons

(includes personal and medical information,
directory of legal, financial, and other professional services,
"Our Children's Friends and Pen Pals," Birthday/Anniversary Card List,
Directory of Friends & Relatives, "Parenting Idea Bank," and
"Scrapbook of Sayings: Our Kids' Cute Expressions"

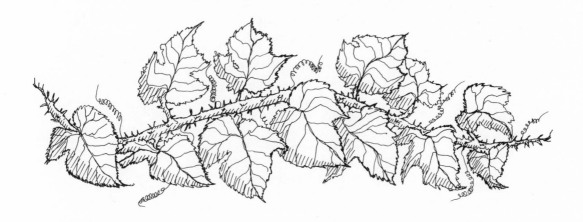

acknowledgments

THE FOLLOWING PEOPLE have contributed professional insight on the family.
My appreciation is extended to them for the energy and interest
they have put into this project.

Gene Bedley, Ed.D.,
1985 PTA Hearst Outstanding Educator of the Year
School Principal
Irvine, California

David Kopp
Editor, *Christian Parenting Today* magazine
Sisters, Oregon

Rick Linamen
Associate Pastor of Adult Ministries
Scottsdale Bible Church
Scottsdale, Arizona

Kay Kuzma, Ed.D.
Child Development Specialist
Redlands, California

Greg Marron, M.S.
Nationally Certified School Psychologist
Bend, Oregon

Elaine McEwan, Ed.D.,
School Principal
Wheaton, Illinois

Clara Schuster, Ph.D., R.N.
Child and Family Development Specialist
Kent State University
Mount Vernon, Ohio

Erroll E. Stephens Jr., Ph.D.
Family, Marriage, and Child Therapist
Portland, Oregon

If we're not drawing closer, we're growing apart

ALONG WITH FIFTY MILLION other Americans I grew up in the fifties, when *family* was the answer. In the seventies, my generation was the first to face the issue of whether or not to have children, and how many children to have. *Family* became the question.

As we pass over the threshold to the nineties, family seems to be vogue once more. But it no longer means what it did when my mom and dad's well-defined roles guided them in raising three children.

I married a modern man who challenged my traditional bent by grabbing the dishcloth out of my hand and expecting me to go out to work for my *own* sake, and for the *world's*. But like many parents these days, I sometimes feel sorry about spending time away from my children, and I feel that a thriving family is more important than a thriving career.

It used to be said, *The hand that rocks the cradle, rules the world.* Girls who grew up wearing poodle skirts and bobby sox are now rocking the cradle with their left hand, while lifting a scalpel, an airbrush, or a business analysis with their right. Boys who grew up in the jukebox era are now expected to change diapers and linens at home, things they never saw their fathers do. Men and women both are caught in the breakers of change: changing vistas and changing attitudes.

Like other parents these days, I must learn to serve both worlds; to live out the ideals of my heritage, yet shed light on uncharted paths for my children, for their sake and the world's. Shuffling a heavily notated appointment book between myself and my husband, Ben, I have to *fight* for empty spaces reserved just for us and our three daughters. Why do I bother? Because, beyond the shifting seas and changing color of the skies, I

have yet to see a sign that anything but *family* is the future of humanity. I have yet to chart a course through anything as wondrous as the laughter of children.

Ben and I are assuming our responsibilities with advantages and resources that were largely lacking in our childhood homes. But, along with other parents we are under pressures as never before. Modern life styles, plus the cumulative effect of an overabundance of choices, directions, and impressions, produce more of what we don't need: stress and fragmentation. In the attempt to lay hold of possibilities, we sometimes sacrifice the basics. We wrestle to have it all, and many of us come away limping.

In my fifteen years of marriage and twelve years of parenthood, I've learned that if my husband, my kids, and I are not drawing closer, we're growing apart. Providing an atmosphere conducive to blossoming relationships and individual growth is not a once and for all accomplishment. It's a process requiring consistent renewal and refinement. I want not only to survive this task, but to enjoy it; to find that it liberates the best in me and draws out qualities that would lie dormant if I had taken off in other directions.

Determining to capture magic moments, I, along with other parents of the nineties, will think strategically about raising families. The few years given to us are crucial, for these are all we have to influence our children and to become, through parenting, mature individuals ourselves before we turn our kids loose in *their* world.

THIS BOOK IS FOR YOU IF...

- in starting a family you were stunned by the thrill of bringing children into the world, but are beginning to realize the magnitude of the task ahead of you

- you see how quickly the years slip by, and how easily kids slide off in their own directions

- you want to build a many-faceted family life that is innovative and buoyant to crisis

- you want the members of your family to be aware of others and aware of needs beyond your front door

- you wonder (in your worst moments!) how you got yourself into parenting predicaments you never imagined possible

- you want to capture the hearts of your children during their years at home so they can face the world with confidence

Why use this book...

SUCCESSFUL CORPORATE MANAGERS use a strategic approach to increase productivity and enhance the work climate. Time is regularly set aside to refocus the corporation's energy and direction. If it is true that *to fail to plan is to plan to fail*, then it is important to *plan* our time, energy, money and emotional resources within the context of those we call *family*.

As my children grow I want an effective, happy result from the task of parenthood. Developing strategies has helped me organize and deal positively with family issues. In the arena of family life, strategic planning means evaluating strengths and weaknesses, opportunities and obstacles; then setting goals and developing a unique family approach to meeting them. *The Intimate Family* presents a format for doing that in your family.

You may be thinking, "We're doing great if we just get the dishes stuffed in the dishwasher and the kids tucked into bed on time!" This planner *will* require more of you than the money you pay for it. The true cost is what you spend in commitment to your spouse and kids, and the dedication you write into these pages yourselves. But the yield on your investment will be well worth it.

The Intimate Family is not the kind of book you will read through and lay aside. It is a book to be written in, filled out and embellished by you and your family. You will want to keep it close to the telephone, the bedside table, or the breakfast nook. You will want to pick it up regularly to record insights and ideas. Working through it you will address such issues as: *What concrete ways can we build self-esteem in our daughter? How will we structure solutions to personality conflicts? How would reorganizing household chores help us have more energy for each other?* I challenge you to use it to enrich the greatest adventure of your lives: drawing closer and growing stronger as a family.

How to use this book...

THE INTIMATE FAMILY is your tool for planning the years you spend raising a family. You'll evaluate practical and emotional issues between you and your spouse, and you and your children. And you'll involve the entire family in the process of establishing workable goals. Here's how:

STEP ONE: Browse through this book and become familiar with it. Get an overview of the process, and talk about that process with your spouse and kids before you start.

STEP TWO: Establish from your very first family meeting a cooperative commitment to keep the project going. If some members of your family resist this process, see it as an opportunity for the rest of you to become creative, and bring them along by proving it can be *fun*.

You might want to skip around in the book. (A teenager might be enticed by talking first about her dreams for the future. A disinterested husband might be invited to bring his experience to the chapter on thinking creatively.)

Serve a choice desert! Put on your favorite music! Start by dancing with your kids or playing a game. Make it an event where everyone has a good time.

STEP THREE: Establish a half-hour date with your spouse each week. Take one chapter at a time and complete the personal family assessment section titled *Couple Time* in that chapter.

STEP FOUR: Establish a regular weekly evening with your children to evaluate family issues by completing the *Family Feedback* and *Kid Talk* sections in that chapter. Write down the dates and times you've established on the planning calendar (next page). Elect one person to fill in the pages of the guidebook.

STEP FIVE: Purchase a small notebook for each member of the family who can read and write. Questions designed for answering individually before discussing are keyed with this symbol: ✍

STEP SIX: Proceed patiently and involve each member of the family as much as possible.

When you have completed the first five parts of the guidebook, you will have defined the challenges you face and the direction you want to go, laying a foundation for *Setting Goals in Key Areas*. Questions designed to refer back to once you begin setting goals in Part VI are keyed like this: ☞

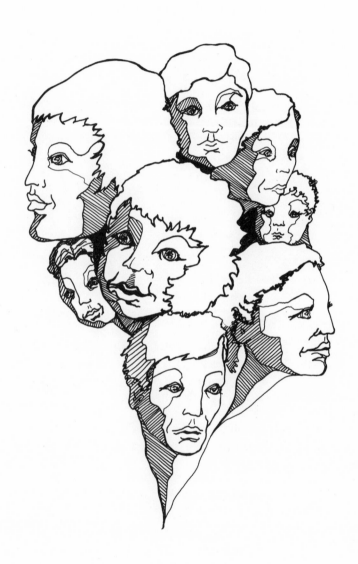

Who We Are

Uncovering Our Heritage

In order to live life forward, we must understand it backward.

SOREN KIERKEGAARD

WE ALL COME to this world with a heritage from the people who lived before us, people who through their beliefs, their social status, their work and play and dreams shaped the values and patterns of our present existence. Our journey cannot be defined by the span of a single generation. It must be seen as a braided cord of human lives from time long gone.

This became real in our own family when we began to explore our heritage. As an intercultural family with European roots on my husband's side and solid American farm stock on mine, we interviewed aunts and uncles, did research in regional archives, gathered old family photos and wrote the story as far back as 250 years. Then we presented a printed copy to our children's grandparents. Since the day we finished the project, our identity and sense of belonging have been strengthened, and our children now look forward with brightened imaginations because they understand where they come from.

Journalist Russell Baker had something like this in mind when he observed, "When Mother was young, with life ahead of her, I had been her future and resented it. Instinctively, I wanted to break free, cease being a creature defined by her time, consign her future to the past, and create my own. Well, I had finally done that, and then with my own children I had seen my exciting future become their boring past....

"I thought that, when I am beyond explaining, my children would want to know what the world was like when my mother was young and I was younger, and we two relics passed together through strange times. I thought I should try to tell them how it was to be young in the time before jet planes, superhighways, H-bombs, and the global village of

14

television." (Russell Baker, *Growing Up*,).

Security comes not so much in where you put down roots as in the people with whom your personal roots are entwined. A sense of belonging and identity equips young people with a stronger sense of self, bringing with it the aptness to say *no* to peer pressure and *yes* to loyalty, trust, and accountability.

In the modern world where kids are often prematurely pushed into responsibilities even adults have difficulty handling, it is more important than ever to pass on to the next generation a sense of rootedness.

Personal Family Assessment

First, it's your turn, Mom. Make a cup of tea and sit down with any records of your family you may have: your baby book, photo albums, a family Bible, notebooks or letters from your parents, or perhaps a box of old pictures. Using these records, fill in the Family History Record (on the following pages) from your side of the family on up to the present, adding information about your marriage and children. You may need to make a phone call or two to an older relative.

Make a date with your husband for a chat about his side of the family. Prepare for this by gathering as many records as possible from his parents, a brother, sister or cousin of his.

When you've completed the Family History Record, gather your children for a Family Roots Event and review with them the results of your research over a tray of appetizers or bowl of popcorn. Ask your kids to fill in some of the information themselves, to tell you all they know or have heard about before you share with them what you've recorded. Continue on into *Kid Talk* and *Family Feedback.* You may not want to go through every question; you may want to just touch on some of them. You may want to dwell a long time on others. But keep the focus on fun and the sense of family identity between you.

The Family Tree

Working your way up from Mom & Dad's heart, write in the names of grandparents and great-grandparents on this family tree.

Record children's names in the lower hearts.

For each PERSON: list name, birth/death dates, and birthplace.
For each COUPLE: list marriage date.

Mom   Dad

OUR FAMILY

Mom & Dad's Occupations:

Mom & Dad's Places of Residence:

How Mom & Dad Met:

Every Family Tree Has Roots

Fill in your Family History Record. Whatever you are unable to complete, you may want to do together with your children — researching and digging up as much historical information as possible.

Family History Record — THE FACTS ABOUT OUR ROOTS

	Places of Residence	Occupations	Ethnic Origins
Mom's Parents:			
_____			
_____			
Dad's Parents:			
_____			
_____			
Mom's Grandparents:			
_____			
_____			
_____			
_____			
Dad's Grandparents:			
_____			
_____			
_____			

Family History Record

ADDING FLESH TO THE BONES OF OUR PAST

- What historically significant events did your parents or grandparents become associated with? (This might include involvement in world events such as wars, earthquakes, Olympic competitions, etc.)

    Dad's Side   Mom's Side

- What furnishings, jewelry, mementos have you inherited from your families? Do you know the history associated with them? Where or how did you get them?

    Dad's Side   Mom's Side

- What are the cultural characteristics of your ethnic backgrounds?

    Dad's Side   Mom's Side

- What were the *places* like where your grandparents/parents raised their families?

  <u>Dad's Side</u>   <u>Mom's Side</u>

- What was that *period of time* like when your grandparents/parents were raising their families?

- How have values and lifestyles changed since then?

☞ How might you and your children discover these things together?
- → Visit the library as a family and borrow pertinent books, period newspapers and magazines. Look for the difference in advertisements, article subject matter, and editorial viewpoint.
- → Visit old family homes, cemeteries, schools.
- → Do interviews with grandparents, aunts and uncles about their childhood and youth, tape them, type them up and put them together with photos and other research material about their lives.
- → Other ways?

✍ *Family Trivia*

Read aloud the questions below, and ask your children (those old enough to write) to jot down their answers in their personal notebooks. This will give them an opportunity to test their knowledge in each area without being influenced by answers of older siblings. Take turns reading answers aloud. (Correct answers can be recorded below.)

Allow those who can't write to participate too.

→ What does your family name mean?

→ Where did your family name originate?

→ What was Mom's maiden name?

→ Where was Mom born?

→ What is Dad's middle name?

→ Who was Dad named after?

→ Where did Mom and Dad grow up?

→ What colleges/universities did they attend?

→ What kind of jobs have Mom and Dad held?

→ What kind of jobs do Mom and Dad have now?

→ How did Mom and Dad meet each other?

→ What time of year did they get married? Where?

→ Where did they go on a honeymoon?

→ How many years have they been married?

What About Grandparents?

- If your grandparents are living, how often do you see them or write to them?

- Should you or could you do this more often?

- What are the advantages to you if you spend time with people who are a generation or two older than you?

- What are the advantages to them? How do you think they feel when you spend time with them?

- If you have no living grandparents, would you consider adopting some through a church, senior citizen organization or rest home?

- If you adopted grandparents, what would you do for them?

- What would you expect them to do for you?

Just for Fun: Family Traits

- What *physical* traits were passed to your family from Mom's side?

  From Dad's side?

- What *character* traits were passed on from Mom's side?

  From Dad's side?

- Which of these are you most proud of, and why?

- How were these traits combined in each of you?

- What three words best describe your family?

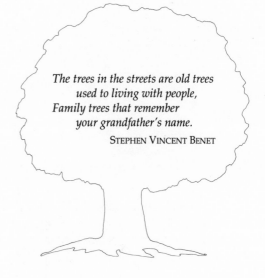

The trees in the streets are old trees
used to living with people,
Family trees that remember
your grandfather's name.

STEPHEN VINCENT BENET

Your Special Places

In the spaces below, describe one or two special places where you have lived and played and made it yours in a personal way; a place you would someday enjoy taking your future grandchildren back to.

Why was (and is) it special?

What happened there to make it so?

(Your kids may enjoy writing here about *their* special places as well.)

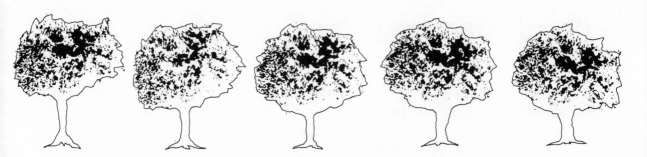

"Tell Me a Story About You"

Use your family history record to inspire your kids to add more flesh to the bones of their past. Have each child ask you one or two of the questions below. Record the stories on tape or take notes here.

- What is the naughtiest thing you ever did?

- What was the most fun you ever had with your parents?

- What was the best present you ever received?

- How did you feel the first time you spent a week away from home by yourself?

- How did you usually spend Sunday afternoons with your family?

- What was the funniest, scariest, or most embarrassing thing that ever happened to you?

- How did you choose your current job/career? Would you do anything differently today?

- How would you describe *your* parents? What kind of people were they?

Your Family Coat of Arms

On the page at right, design a coat of arms representing your family's traits and accomplishments. Without concern for artistic results, have each child draft a design for each of the six areas shown on the coat of arms. Here are suggested guidelines for the content of each the six parts:

1. Draw something you like to do with your family.
2. Draw the place in your house where you feel most at home.
3. Draw something that belongs to your family that everybody is proud of.
4. Draw your family pets.
5. Draw one of your favorite family celebrations.
6. Write the three words that best describe your family when you are most happy together.

Based on the designs from each member of the family, draw a large family coat of arms. Let the younger children color it. Cover it with transparent contact paper and hang it in a prominent place. One family made copies, laminated them and use them daily as placemats.

Fill in the coat of arms on the next page just like the one you've made.

A Family Time Line

Chart the major events in your family's history on the time line below. Start from the date of your marriage. Write in significant happenings like births and deaths, moves to new homes, acquiring pets, unique family celebrations, illnesses or accidents, and special family memories.

Our Marriage:
19___

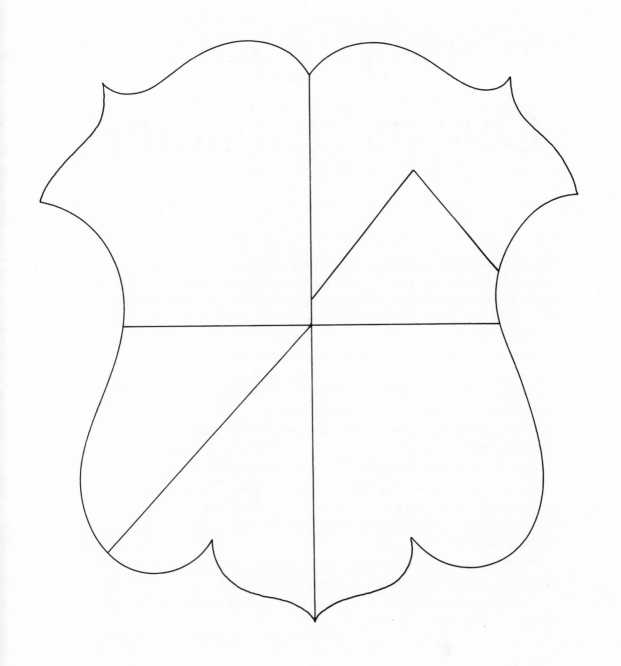

the present

Appreciating Our Individuality

LOOKING AT IT LIGHTLY

Then, too, rearing three children is like growing a cactus, a gardenia and a tubful of impatiens. Each needs varying amounts of water, sunlight and pruning. Were I to be absolutely fair, I would have to treat each child as if he or she were absolutely identical to the other siblings, and there would be no profit for anyone in that.

The other afternoon, for example, my daughter tried to pry out a later–than–usual curfew for a weekend evening. Being unsuccessful, she resorted to accusing me of being a hypocrite — after all, her older brother was allowed to stay out later when he was her age.

She was right. I had allowed him to stay out later, a permission I would not have given him if I knew then what I know now. But I did not mention this to her.

"Do you think that you're different from your brother?" I asked her.

My daughter is no dummy. She could see the corner I was constructing for her. How many times had she told me that she certainly was not like her brother, the implication being that she had more class.

"No...well, yes," she replied.

"Well, of course you're different," I confirmed, ignoring the first half of her answer. "And that's why I treat you differently. Otherwise, it wouldn't be fair."

I hated myself for being so manipulative. But when one is trying to raise children, sometimes foul is fair.

PHYLLIS THEROUX, *Night Lights*

* * *

I WAS GLOWING, a first-time mother with a baby girl one day old. I was certain no baby had ever been more beautiful than mine. I was certain no mother had ever been as good as I would be. But when my perfect baby refused to nurse and screamed in protest each time I tried, the nurses told me matter of factly, "You'll have trouble with this one!"

I dismissed their summation. After all, what did they know?

Twelve years later, I have to give them credit. They *knew* what they were talking about. I've had to fight for every inch of motherhood Tirza has allowed me.

My experience with Tirza prepared me for difficulty when our second child came along. But to my amazement, Lea never protested or complained about anything. Quiet and dreamy, she almost worried me. I thought something must be wrong with her since she wasn't like her strong-willed sister. By the time our third daughter was born, I'd begun to catch on — each child is totally different and totally wonderful.

In the interaction of the children I have seen gifts I had not recognized in their personalities as infants, and I've seen how family life works like a grind stone to smooth the jagged edges of their temperaments — and mine. Each child is a challenge to raise because of their individuality, and even the most challenging child can be rewarding.

Educator Elaine McEwan writes that she was a challengingly active child "before pediatricians and psychologists turned hyperactivity into a liability. As I grew older, it became an asset. I just needed to have my energies channeled. And that was an exhausting job for all of the people who loved me — my parents, an aunt, a bachelor uncle, and two sets of grandparents. Thank goodness for these wonderful people who enjoyed my chatter and energy and were willing to put up with me" (Elaine McEwan, *Superkids?*).

Gregg L. Marron, an educational psychologist in Bend, Oregon, suggests that families try to build upon personality assessments and, in cases of conflicting temperaments, to structure patterns of interaction that allow for personal expression while avoiding personality clashes.

"For example," Gregg says, "if laid-back parents happen to have a hyper child, they can allow for differences by establishing safety valves as they map out family strategies. The parents can make sure the child has an opportunity to explore and satisfy his curiosity within structured boundaries that are set down beforehand. And parents should schedule regular intervals of relief from the intensity of such a child."

Combinations of personality and temperament can be complex, but if people who live together understand even a little about what makes the others tick, they become more tolerant and are better able to challenge and encourage each other.

Tips for Parenting First Borns or Only Children

1. Don't reinforce your child's already ingrained perfectionistic tendencies by being an "improver" on everything he says and does.
2. Realize your child has a need to know exactly what the rules are by taking time to lay things out "from A to Z."
3. Recognize your child's first place in the family. He should get some special privileges to go along with the additional responsibilities.

Tips for Parenting the Middle Child

1. Recognize that many middle children are prone to avoid sharing how they really feel and are least likely to insist on a fair share of your attention. Set aside times for just the two of you to talk.
2. Take extra care to make your child feel special by asking for his opinion, letting him choose, etc.
3. Set up some regular, simple privileges your child can count on having or doing every day or every week, something that is his exclusive territory.

Tips for Parenting the Last-Born Child

1. Be sure your last born has a fair share of responsibilities around the house. Last borns are masters at ducking out of the work that needs to be done; and are so "helpless" that other family members often decide it's easier to do it themselves.
2. Statistics show your last-born child is least likely to be disciplined. Make notes on how you held the older kids responsible and enforce the same bedtime and other rules.
3. Make a big deal out of your child's accomplishments and be sure he gets a fair share of "marquee time" on the refrigerator door.

(adapted from KEVIN LEMAN's
The Birth Order Book)

All About Me

Record the following information about yourself. Before reading your responses to each other, see if you can guess your spouse's answers.

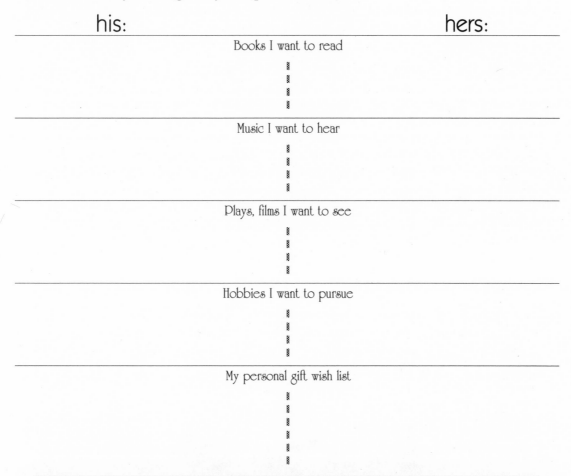

his: hers:

Books I want to read

Music I want to hear

Plays, films I want to see

Hobbies I want to pursue

My personal gift wish list

THE QUESTIONS, activities and discussion on these pages will help you explore the patterns of experience woven into the lives of your family members as well as the personality characteristics defining each of you. By doing so, you'll be painting a family portrait worthy of handing down to the next generation. Capitalizing on the qualities that set you apart as individuals as well as those which you hold in common will help your family set reachable goals, seek unique aspirations, and bring understanding to relationships.

his: _____ hers: _____

Personal projects
I want to pursue

Gift ideas I think will suit HER for...

her birthday:

Christmas:

our wedding anniversary:

Valentine's Day:

Mother's Day:

our special day:

for no special reason at all

Gift ideas I think will suit HIM for...

his birthday:

Christmas:

our wedding anniversary:

Valentine's Day:

Father's Day:

our special day:

for no special reason at all:

his: hers:

3 unusual experiences from
my childhood that make
me unique

3 things in my life
I'm proudest of

Events in my life that
changed me most

3 things I was hesitant
to try — but managed
to succeed at

3 words I would like to have
said about me

The 3 most influential
people in my life

31

☞ *Our Personalities*

It's fun to look at yourself from an objective perspective. In order to get an overview of your personality preferences, read the statements listed below. Check those with which you strongly agree about yourself. (There are no right or wrong answers, since there are no categorically "good" or "bad" personality types.)

After thinking about yourself in these terms, set aside fifteen minutes to talk with your spouse about your personalities and how they affect your relationship.

(Questions adapted from *Type Talk* by OTTO KROEGER and JANET M. THUESEN)

HOW DO YOU USUALLY INTERACT WITH THE WORLD—

as an Extrovert...

HE SHE
- ☐ ☐ Tends to talk first, think later
- ☐ ☐ Doesn't mind distractions or interruptions
- ☐ ☐ Is approachable by strangers and friends
- ☐ ☐ Enjoys parties with lots of people in preference to intimate conversations
- ☐ ☐ Has a need to bounce thoughts off others
- ☐ ☐ Finds listening more difficult than talking
- ☐ ☐ Tends to need affirmation from others

or as an Introvert?

HE SHE
- ☐ ☐ Wants to think about things before answering
- ☐ ☐ Prefers peace and quiet to background noise, music, talking, etc.
- ☐ ☐ Is a good listener and expects the same of others
- ☐ ☐ Prefers special occasions with a few close friends
- ☐ ☐ Sometimes longs to express thoughts more forcefully
- ☐ ☐ Sets a premium on time alone
- ☐ ☐ Is easily irritated by chatter and repetitious talk

IS YOUR GENERAL ORIENTATION TO LIFE—

as a Judger...

HE SHE
- ☐ ☐ Always seems to be waiting for others
- ☐ ☐ Has a place for everything
- ☐ ☐ Has a schedule and follows it throughout the day
- ☐ ☐ Doesn't like surprises
- ☐ ☐ Keeps lists and uses them
- ☐ ☐ Thrives on order
- ☐ ☐ Likes to work things through to completion

or as a Perceiver?

HE SHE
- ☐ ☐ Is easily distracted
- ☐ ☐ Loves to explore the unknown
- ☐ ☐ Often is accused of being disorganized
- ☐ ☐ Depends on last-minute spurts of energy
- ☐ ☐ Values creativity over neatness
- ☐ ☐ Usually turns work into play
- ☐ ☐ Likes to keep options open before making a commitment

HOW DO YOU USUALLY MAKE DECISIONS—
as a Thinker...
or as a Feeler?

HE SHE

☐ ☐ Is able to stay cool and calm in upsetting situations

☐ ☐ Feels fair treatment by others is more important than happiness

☐ ☐ Enjoys discussions as a way to expand intellectual horizons

☐ ☐ Is more firm-minded than gentle-hearted

☐ ☐ Prides himself or herself on objectivity

☐ ☐ Is impressed with the logical and scientific

☐ ☐ Remembers numbers more readily than names

HE SHE

☐ ☐ Considers other people's feelings when making decisions

☐ ☐ Believes "love" cannot be defined

☐ ☐ Tends to accommodate others at the expense of his or her comfort

☐ ☐ Enjoys providing services, though he or she may be taken advantage of

☐ ☐ Prefers harmony over clarity

☐ ☐ Sometimes wonders why no one seems to care about him or her

☐ ☐ Often is accused of taking things too personally

HOW DO YOU USUALLY GATHER INFORMATION—
as a Sensor...
or as an Intuitive?

HE SHE

☐ ☐ Likes specific answers to your specific questions

☐ ☐ Would rather do something than think about it

☐ ☐ Needs tangible results in daily job or activities

☐ ☐ Would rather work with facts and figures than ideas and theories

☐ ☐ Does not believe in the value of fantasy

☐ ☐ Requires detailed instructions rather than vague guidelines

☐ ☐ Interprets things and words literally

HE SHE

☐ ☐ Tends to think about several things simultaneously

☐ ☐ Is more excited about where he or she is going than where he or she is

☐ ☐ Finds details rather boring

☐ ☐ Believes time is relative

☐ ☐ Enjoys figuring out how things work for the sheer joy of it

☐ ☐ Does not accept things at face value

☐ ☐ Tends to give general answers to questions

- In what ways are your personalities different from each other?
- In what ways are your personalities the same?
- How can you maximize your similarities?
- How can you use your differences constructively?
- In what ways do you complement one another?
- Which personality preferences do you appreciate most about your spouse?
- Which ones do you find most difficult to live with? (Try to describe them in an objective way.)

All About Me

(Instructions for each child:) Put your name in one of the boxes on this page and the next. Then record the information asked for about yourself. Afterward, read your answers out loud to one another. (You may want to photocopy these pages now before filling it out, so you'll have copies to complete when you're older.)

favorite
subject in
school

favorite
television
program

most
prized
possession

books
I want
to read

music
I want
to hear

plays and
films I want
to see

hobbies
I want to
pursue

my
personal
gift wish
list

personal
projects I
want to
pursue

gift ideas
for Mom

gift ideas
for Dad

gift Ideas
for others

Our Kids' Temperaments

Kids, read the statements listed below. Then check those that are *most true* of yourself. (There are no right or wrong answers.) Before answering, write your initials above one of the columns of boxes, and mark all your answers in that column.

(Adapted from *Know Your Child* by Dr. Stella Chess and Dr. Alexander Thomas)

□ □ □ 1. When I come home from school I like to go outside and play an active game.

□ □ □ 2. I like to play in my room, do jigsaw puzzles, read, or draw.

□ □ □ 3. I wake up like clockwork every morning at the same time. My mom never needs to wake me.

□ □ □ 4. Sometimes I fall asleep right after dinner. Other times I could keep going until way past bedtime.

□ □ □ 5. I make lots of new friends on the first day of school. I'm usually one of the first to get to know the new kids in the class.

□ □ □ 6. I always feel like I'll never catch on when we start something in class that's brand new, like fractions or driver's education.

□ □ □ 7. When I go somewhere I've never gone before or meet people I've never seen before, I feel comfortable and get involved quickly.

□ □ □ 8. When we moved it took me a long time to get used to the neighborhood and make friends.

□ □ □ 9. If I bang my head or someone pulls my hair it doesn't bother me much.

□ □ □ 10. I hate wearing clothes that scratch or irritate my skin, or that have tight waistbands.

□ □ □ 11. If my mom gives me a piece of toast that's a little burnt, I just eat around the burnt part.

□ □ □ 12. My parents sometimes say, "You're always complaining. Why do you make everything a big deal?"

□ □ □ 13. Even when I fail at something I don't get very upset. At least, I don't show it.

□ □ □ 14. If I don't get what I want, I let everybody around me know how I feel.

□ □ □ 15. Sometimes I really want something badly, but before long I've forgotten about it.

□ □ □ 16. Doing my homework takes a long time because other things tend to distract me.

□ □ □ 17. I like to figure out math problems all by myself.

□ □ □ 18. When I'm learning something new, like ice skating, I usually feel like giving up right away.

□ □ □ 19. I like to read, but only for a short time.

□ □ □ 20. If I have a part in the school play, I'll spend hours rehearsing for it.

Temperament Characteristics

Once again using a column marked by your initials, go through the list below and check the *one* characteristic *in each pair* that you feel best describes you. (These traits correspond to the statements you looked at on the opposite page; the number after each trait refers to the matching statement from that list. You may want to refer to that list to help you think about the traits below. You may also want help from your parents for the meaning of some of these terms.)

☐	☐	☐	High Energy *(1)*
☐	☐	☐	Low Energy *(2)*
☐	☐	☐	Spontaneous *(3)*
☐	☐	☐	Rhythmical *(4)*
☐	☐	☐	Approachable *(5)*
☐	☐	☐	Withdrawn *(6)*
☐	☐	☐	Adaptable *(7)*
☐	☐	☐	Dislikes change *(8)*
☐	☐	☐	High Sensory Threshold *(9)*
☐	☐	☐	Low Sensory Threshold *(10)*
☐	☐	☐	Stable Moods *(11)*
☐	☐	☐	Moody *(12)*
☐	☐	☐	Calm *(13)*
☐	☐	☐	Emotional *(14)*
☐	☐	☐	Easily Distracted *(15)*
☐	☐	☐	Not Easily Distracted *(16)*
☐	☐	☐	Persistent *(17)*
☐	☐	☐	Gives Up Easily *(18)*
☐	☐	☐	Short Attention Span *(19)*
☐	☐	☐	Long Attention Span *(20)*

✍ In going through the lists on these pages, you've probably learned somethings you didn't know before about yourself and your siblings. Record in your personal notebook your answers to the questions below.

- What are the primary personality differences between you and your siblings?
- What are the personality similarities between you and your siblings?
- What qualities do you admire in your brothers and sisters?

☞ How can we minimize our differences?

☞ How can we relate to each other positively instead of clashing?

☞ How can we make the most of our similarities?

Just for Fun: Self Portraits

In the spaces on these pages (use one space for each family member), record how everyone completes these sentences:

1. My personality could best be described by the color…
2. My personality could best be described as the taste of…
3. The cartoon or Sesame Street character that reminds me most of myself is…
4. What I like best about being me is…
☞ 5. The thing I wish was different about my personality is…
6. The movie character most like me is…
7. If I could be like any public figure, I'd want to be like…
8. My hero is…
9. The animal that's most like me is _____ because…
10. My best day ever was…
11. The gift I've cherished most is…
12. The best compliment I've ever received was…
13. My favorite relative is _____ because…
14. My dream vacation would be…

name

name

name

name

name

39

Build Up Character Strengths

Read the positive character qualities llisted below, and beside them write the initials of any family members who come to mind. (The negative characteristics listed may be what you think of first about someone — but use that negative trait to help you realize the person's matching strength.)

POSITIVE	NEGATIVE	POSITIVE	NEGATIVE
Analytical	Insincere	Generous	Wasteful
Assertive	Domineering	Imaginative	Day-dreaming
Communicative	Overtalkative	Listening	Noncommunicative
Concerned	Worrying	Loyal	Idolizing
Confident	Self-sufficient	Moral	Judgmental
Counseling	"Know-it-all"	Obedient	Over-dependent
Courageous	Reckless	Open-minded	Indecisive
Curious	Nosey	Optimistic	Unrealistic
Determined	Stubborn	Orderly	Perfectionistic
Diplomatic	Weak-willed	Sensitive	Oversensitive
Effective	Rigid	Spontaneous	Undisciplined
Encouraging	Flattering	Stable	Dull
Expressive	Flowery	Straightforward	Harsh
Forgiving	Over-lenient	Thrifty	Stingy

(adapted from *Orphans At Home* by Joe White)

☞ (To talk about together:) How can you encourage each other's strengths? (Beside each person's initials below, write down how you can encourage him or her.)

———————

———————

———————

———————

———————

☞ What character or personality traits would you like to develop in yourself?

More about Temperaments

"Our temperaments are like vast oceans. We all have shallow and deep areas. The shoreline might be jagged or smooth. The surf might be turbulent and crashing, or calm and rhythmic. But beneath the surface there is a great variety of life.

"The combination of these forms of life, the ways we react to the world, can be seen as our personality types. Intuitive parents have known for a long time what has only recently been documented: that contrasts in personality and temperament lead to conflicts for which no one is to blame. We can't genetically plan for complimentary personalities. We can't take our child back to the hospital because she has a temperament that cramps our style. But we can allow for differences and plan helpful strategies..."

GREGG MARRON

☞ What Kind of Family Are You?

- What personality preferences and character strengths characterize your family as a whole?

- How is your family different from your neighbors' or friends' families?

- In what ways is that an asset?

Identifying Our Family Season

SOMEDAY AND YESTERDAY

Someday when the kids are grown, things are going to be a lot different. The garage won't be full of bikes, electric train tracks on plywood, sawhorses surrounded by chunks of two-by-fours, nails, a hammer and saw, unfinished "experimental projects," and the rabbit cage....

Someday when the kids are grown, the kitchen will be incredibly neat. The sink will stay free of sticky dishes, the garbage disposal won't get choked on rubber bands or paper cups, the refrigerator won't be clogged with nine bottles of milk, and we won't lose the tops to jelly jars, catsup bottles, the peanut butter, the margarine, or the mustard....

Someday when the kids are grown, my lovely wife will actually have time to get dressed leisurely. A long hot bath (without three panic interruptions), time to do her nails (even toenails if she pleases!) without answering a dozen questions and reviewing spelling words....

Someday when the kids are grown, the instrument called a "telephone" will actually be available. It won't look like it's growing from a teenager's ear. It will simply hang there...silently and amazingly available! It will be free of lipstick, human saliva, mayonnaise, cornchip crumbs, and toothpicks stuck in those little holes.

Someday when the kids are grown, I'll be able to see through the car windows. Fingerprints, tongue licks, sneaker footprints, and dog tracks (nobody knows how) will be conspicuous by their absence...we won't sit on jacks or crayons any more, the tank will not always be somewhere between empty and fumes and (glory to God!) I won't have to clean up dog messes another time.

Someday when the kids are grown, we will return to normal conversations. You know, just plain American talk. "Gross" won't punctuate every sentence seven times. "Yuk!" will not be heard. "Hurry up, I gotta go!" will not accompany the banging of fists on the bathroom door....

Someday when the kids are grown, we won't run out of toilet tissue. My wife won't lose her keys. We won't forget to shut the refrigerator door. I won't have to dream up new ways of diverting attention from the gumball machine ...or promise to kiss the rabbit goodnight...or have to take a number to get a word in at the supper table....

Yes, someday when the kids are grown, things are going to be a lot different. One by one they'll leave our nest, and the place will begin to resemble order and maybe even a touch of elegance. The clink of china and silver will be heard on occasion. The crackling of the fireplaces will echo through the hallway. The phone will be strangely silent. The house will be quiet...and calm...and always clean...and empty...and filled with memories...and lonely...and we won't like that at all. And we'll spend our time not looking forward to Someday but looking back to Yesterday. And thinking, Maybe we can baby-sit the grandkids and get some life back in this place for a change....

CHUCK SWINDOLL, *Home: Where Life Makes Up Its Mind*

* * *

I GREW UP in Southern California where the change of nature was only faintly noticed. Sandals and sun dresses were never relegated to the back of the closet. Each autumn when new fashion magazines appeared on supermarket shelves I felt a twinge of envy, for I never had reason to dress in bright colored wools or wear the lavish overclothes displayed on their covers.

When I moved, married and established a family elsewhere, several snowy winters passed before I garnered a proper winter wardrobe. It was even longer before I caught on that coats and sweaters must be packed in mothballs for the summer if they are to last until the following year. Clothes must be organized around *seasons* to keep them from falling apart and to keep shelves and drawers from becoming a jumble.

My husband and I have had to reorganize our lifestyle about as often as our closets. According to the ages and development of our children, Ben and I have taken turns as housewife and househusband, as well as alternately working free-lance from our home, and working full-time and part-time outside the home. We've made sacrifices according to our family *season*. One parent at home in the children's early years meant rinsing, washing, hanging and folding muslin diapers thousands of times. It meant renting a farm house (with extended family of mice), picking up baby equipment at thrift stores, and vacationing in our own backyard. Our borrowed motto was *Use it up, wear it out, make it do or do without!*

After all three children were in school, we both accepted full-time jobs and the hassles of juggled work schedules in order to lessen the financial stress. Throughout the years, seasonal changes have forced us to recognize both our limitations and our potential while working toward our goal — to establish a family and raise thriving kids.

Identification of the temporary limits of our resources and the boundaries of our responsibilities have helped Ben and me deal with the demands placed on us, while we make our kids aware *it won't always be like this* in some cases, or *we will always do it this way* in others.

There always seems to be a longing forward and a looking back as we make the transitions from season to season. I like the way John Powell describes the emotional significance and poignancy of these changes: "Life is a death-resurrection cycle. In every moment there is a death, a leaving what has been, and a birth, a stepping into what is and will be. We must leave things behind: the warmth of our mothers' wombs, privileged infant status, childhood toys, the irresponsible joys of youth, the protection of family and dependent status, jobs, locations, etc. And in the end, we gradually lose our physical strength, our teeth, hearing and vision. There is a constant emotional tension in most people between wanting to go back and reclaim what has been and an eagerness to embrace the new." (John Powell, *The Secret of Staying in Love* p.182-183)

Personal Family Assessment

Change really does add spice to life. Children love the rites associated with the entry into each new season. They thrive on the variety displayed in nature's changes. *Family* seasons should bring the same kind of anticipation to our lives. If the rites defining the changes are celebrated and treasured, we'll be setting a positive example for our children who, growing quickly, will soon be taking their place in an adult world that might otherwise seem cold and unfriendly.

☞ *Establishing Milestones As Husbands and Wives*

Write your answers to the following questions in the form of a love letter to your spouse. Allow ten minutes to write, then trade notebooks and read each other's answers. Set aside ten minutes more to talk about what you have written.

- What are the five most significant milestones you and your spouse have passed together? Why was each significant?
- ☞ What are the three most important decisions you need to make in the next year? Why are they important?
- Toward what choices are you leaning in each decision? What would help you to make wise decisions?
- ☞ Describe what you want life to be like when you are seventy years old. What do you want your life together to be like at that time? What steps should you be taking today to get there?

(Adapted from Dennis and Barbara Rainey's The Questions Book)

Hers:

His:

Bein' a Kid Doesn't Last Forever

Use your initials to label one of the boxes below. Then inside the box, complete these sentences:

- Sometimes I wish I was still a baby because...
- ☞ Sometimes I wish I was older than I am now because...
- When I am grown up I will look back at these days and remember...
- What I like best about being a kid is...

Family Seasons

- What season characterizes your family right now?

    __ Married without children
    __ Just starting a family (the baby-comes-first stage)
    __ The wonderful middle years (children are young and dependent on parents, but old enough to have plenty of their own ideas and plans)
    __ With preteen and early teenage children (they're starting to pull away in different directions, are strongly influenced by peers, but still need a strong support line to Mom and Dad)
    __ With older teenage children…making long steps toward independence and autonomy; (home is becoming a backdrop to their lives)
    __ The empty-nest period (the childhood home is important as a place to come back to for approval, for relaxation, and to get in touch with family)

- Describe your current family season in your own words.

- What are the advantages of this family season?

- What is the most difficult struggle of this season?

Family Seasons — *continued*

- What are the primary decisions you need to make in this season?

  about work:

  about childcare:

  about grandparents:

  about education:

  about discipline:

  about other areas:

- What are some of your favorite memories from the seasons your family has already passed through?

- What lessons have you learned from the seasons you have already passed through?

- How long until your family season changes once again?

☞ What would you like to accomplish as a family before then?

Family Changes

- What things now affecting your family's lifestyles, priorities, and values are likely to be different in the future? How will they be different?

- Check which changes you have made during the last year (or plan to make within the next year):

__ change employment	__ have a child
__ buy a home	__ receive a promotion
__ move	__ start a business
__ sell property	__ change schools or graduate
__ receive an inheritance	__ other major changes

☞ Star the items checked above that could threaten your family unity.

☞ What can your family do to make these changes enhance togetherness?

Anticipating
the Coming Season

- Describe your life the way you expect it to be one year from now.

- How old will your children be? How will they have changed?

- What are the chances you will be living in the same home and pursuing the same career one year from now? __99% __75% __50% __25%

- Describe your life the way you expect it to be five years from now.

- How old will your children be? How will they have changed?

- What are the chances you will be living in the same home and pursuing the same career five years from now? __99% __75% __50% __25%

☞ In what ways might the world have changed? In what ways may you need to adapt your lifestyle to these changes?

Making the Most of Who We Are

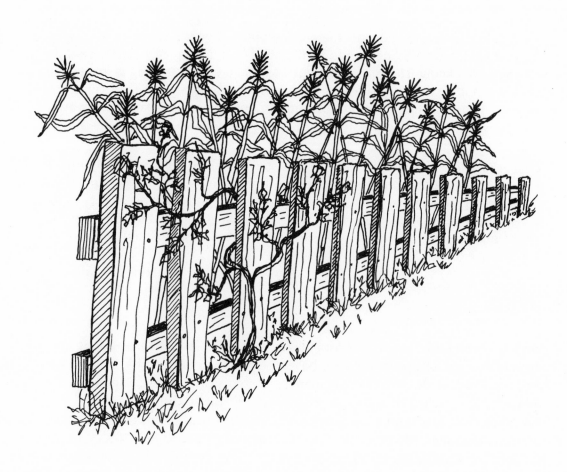

Building Love and Friendship

THE WORK OF LOVE

And this getting to know another, and getting to know yourself — in ways too profound, too revealing ever to be plumbed outside of love — is the most daring work I know. Those who think of it as sheltered and lacking in imagination know not of what they speak. It takes far more emotional courage to lay open your heart to another, more fortitude to unmask another and find ways to enjoy the person who is there, than it ever does to dance away and cry defeat....

An old gardener once said to me, standing over his sweetpea border, its various pinks and purples all rippling in the summer wind, "You plant and water and mulch and weed and water and mulch and weed again season after season, and what do you get? A froth!" And I laughed with him knowing what he said was true of love as well as flowers. It takes a lot of mulch, love does, to produce a froth."

MERLE SHAIN, *Courage My Love*

THE PASTOR WHO performed the marriage ceremony for my husband and me was an experienced counselor, having presided over the weddings of many intercultural couples. He told me, "Marlee, go to your husband's country and learn his language. If you don't, you'll never know your husband." Two weeks after the wedding we did go to Denmark.

I figured we'd be there for a year, plenty of time to learn the language and get to know Ben. Little did I dream it would be seven years before I spoke Danish fluently. Little did I imagine that twelve years in Ben's culture would only launch my exploration of his soul.

The pastor who counseled us was wiser than I was ready to admit at the time. But I know now that his wise counsel goes for every couple — even those coming from similar backgrounds. Most often, a husband and wife will speak two different languages. And those who intend to walk in the same direction, side by side, for a lifetime must learn to communicate effectively, and become intimately acquainted with each other's personal culture.

Such an understanding relationship between parents will influence the relationships between their children more profoundly than efforts to prevent sibling wars by pleading for peace, untangling squabbles, or demanding conformity to rules. E. E. Stephens Jr. of Montavilla Counseling Center in Portland, Oregon, says: "When parents bring children to my office because of behavioral problems, ninety percent of the time the problems of the children are merely reflections of difficulties in the marriage. A strong marriage is critical for the emotional stability and development of children."

Emotional intimacy within the home begins in the marriage relationship and develops or withers there. It is an ongoing process, requiring a sound investment of personal attention. The last couple of decades have seen many couples turning toward each other for brief periods of time until driven off once more in a myriad of directions by fickle winds. Those who have failed to make even simple efforts declare that love has let them down; in fact, they have quietly and peacefully neglected to cultivate whatever had been held in common. Others have recognized that the search for success and instant happiness is shallow, that becoming an intimate family is worth the imagination, the effort, the water and mulch required.

Perhaps, in the years ahead of us, Ben and I will create a new language from the two we spoke before our lives were joined. That language will interpret, for our children and future grandchildren, the enormous value of the friendship and love that building and cultivating together produces.

Personal Family Assessment

Living together for years can create an illusion of intimacy. One husband stated boldly, "My wife knows I love her because I told her so the day we married! And I've spent years proving it by paying the bills and emptying the garbage."

Do you know what your spouse needs to hear from you? Do you know what makes your wife feel loved? Do you know of what your husband appreciates most about your marriage?

Do you know what makes your son or daughter feel important?

Can you think of a common household situation that dramatizes the stuff of real family relationships? A single dad clarified his feelings by posing a simple and succinct question: "Do you smell dinner burning?" What about your feelings?

How Important Do You Feel?

Answer the questions below as they relate to your relationship with your spouse.

his: hers:

I feel proud of you when you…

I feel proud of myself when you…

I feel loved by you when…

I most enjoy being with you when we…

I feel optimistic about overcoming our problems when…

If I could change one thing about our marriage, it would be…

The thing I appreciate most about our marriage is…

A time I remember when you made me feel important to you was when…

My personal way of making love talk is…

	HIS answers		HER answers
The items checked at right are what I feel to be the strongest competitors to closeness in our marriage:	☐	your career	☐
	☐	your relationships at work	☐
	☐	your friends	☐
	☐	your hobbies	☐
	☐	your possessions	☐
	☐	your community or church obligations	☐
	☐	our children	☐
	☐	our house	☐

Read each other's answers in the box above before going on to answer these:

☞ How can we use the time we have together to the best advantage?

- When can we make time to be alone? Where?

- What would we like to do?
  - __ talk about practical things (What would you like to talk about?)
  - __ talk about emotional issues (What would you like to talk about?)
  - __ play together: golf, fish, ski, jog, dance, picnic
  - __ dress up and dine out
  - __ make love
  - __ go to a movie, play, or concert we can discuss afterward
  - __ other activities

☞ In what ways can our emotional intimacy best be enhanced?

☞ How can we make our relationship more romantic?
(List at least five ideas.)

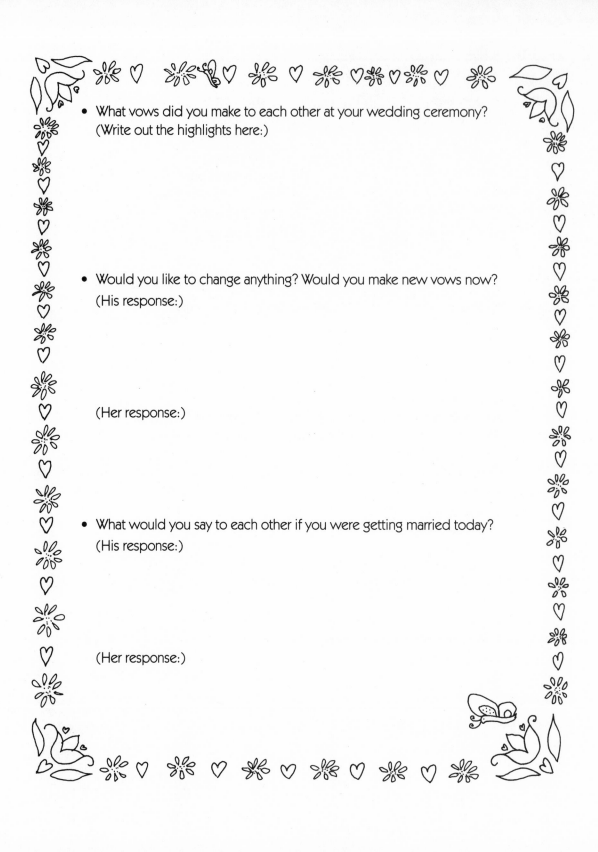

- What vows did you make to each other at your wedding ceremony? (Write out the highlights here:)

- Would you like to change anything? Would you make new vows now? (His response:)

(Her response:)

- What would you say to each other if you were getting married today? (His response:)

(Her response:)

☞ *Building Blocks to Trust and Responsibility*

❏ *Commitment* — Name two different ways to express your loyalty and commitment to your spouse, speaking the language he or she understands.

❏ *Clarification of goals* — What do you expect from your marriage? What do you expect from your spouse?

❏ *Communication* — How much time together with your spouse will you commit to spend each day this week? Each week this month? What is the best, most convenient time for you to meet? What topics do you want to talk about over the next six months? (Make a list of these topics in your journal.)

❏ *Listening* — Are there areas of conversation in which it is difficult for you to listen without becoming defensive? What are these? (Write a letter to your spouse about one of these topics, then read the letter aloud without comment before discussing it.)

❏ *Support and encouragement* — In which two areas of life do you most need the ongoing support and encouragement of your spouse?

❏ *Respect for personal rights* — In what area does your spouse need the freedom to be or to do the things that enhance his or her own identity? What will you do to make sure your spouse's personal rights are protected?

❏ *Expressions of affection* — Write down the two expressions of affection that mean the most to you.

How Important Do You Feel?

Mark your initials on one of the telephones. Inside the cord, write a **+** if you feel more important than each item listed. Write a **−** if you feel less important, and **=** if you feel equally important.

TO MY DAD, I feel more (+)
or less (-) important than:

☐ his job ☐ his tools or stereo equipment
☐ his friends ☐ his rest ☐ his hobbies
☐ his car ☐ his relationship with Mom
☐ his work around the house ☐ his sports
☐ his club or organization meetings
I would feel more important to my dad if…

TO MY MOM, I feel more (+)
or less (-) important than:

☐ her job ☐ her housework ☐ her friends
☐ her rest ☐ her clothes and accessories
☐ her relationship with Dad ☐ her hobbies
☐ her housework ☐ her furniture
☐ her club or organization meetings
I would feel more important to my mom if…

TO MY DAD, I feel more (+)
or less (-) important than:

☐ his job ☐ his tools or stereo equipment
☐ his friends ☐ his rest ☐ his hobbies
☐ his car ☐ his relationship with Mom
☐ his work around the house ☐ his sports
☐ his club or organization meetings
I would feel more important to my dad if…

TO MY MOM, I feel more (+)
or less (-) important than:

☐ her job ☐ her housework ☐ her friends
☐ her rest ☐ her clothes and accessories
☐ her relationship with Dad ☐ her hobbies
☐ her housework ☐ her furniture
☐ her club or organization meetings
I would feel more important to my mom if…

TO MY DAD, I feel more (+)
or less (-) important than:

☐ his job ☐ his tools or stereo equipment
☐ his friends ☐ his rest ☐ his hobbies
☐ his car ☐ his relationship with Mom
☐ his work around the house ☐ his sports
☐ his club or organization meetings
I would feel more important to my dad if…

TO MY MOM, I feel more (+)
or less (-) important than:

☐ her job ☐ her housework ☐ her friends
☐ her rest ☐ her clothes and accessories
☐ her relationship with Dad ☐ her hobbies
☐ her housework ☐ her furniture
☐ her club or organization meetings
I would feel more important to my mom if…

Kids Rate Parents on Skills

Kids, rate your parents in the areas below on a scale from 1 (= "does not meet my needs") to 10 (= "fully meets my needs"). Write your initials above the column you use for your answers.

<<<Evaluate Mom on left   Evaluate Dad on right>>>

☐ ☐ ☐	1. makes time to talk to me			☐ ☐ ☐
☐ ☐ ☐	2. listens to how I *feel*			☐ ☐ ☐
☐ ☐ ☐	3. keeps my secrets			☐ ☐ ☐
☐ ☐ ☐	4. gets close enough to look me in the eye			☐ ☐ ☐
☐ ☐ ☐	5. uses *Please* and *Thank You* with me			☐ ☐ ☐
☐ ☐ ☐	6. praises and encourages me often			☐ ☐ ☐
☐ ☐ ☐	7. gives me plenty of hugs and pats on the back			☐ ☐ ☐
☐ ☐ ☐	8. is happy and enthusiastic about our family			☐ ☐ ☐
☐ ☐ ☐	9. helps me learn how to act in new situations			☐ ☐ ☐
☐ ☐ ☐	10. helps me deal with my problems			☐ ☐ ☐
☐ ☐ ☐	11. finds out the facts before accusing me			☐ ☐ ☐
☐ ☐ ☐	12. helps me set goals for my life			☐ ☐ ☐
☐ ☐ ☐	13. plays with me			☐ ☐ ☐
☐ ☐ ☐	14. models a cheerful attitude about housework			☐ ☐ ☐
☐ ☐ ☐	15. admits it when wrong			☐ ☐ ☐
☐ ☐ ☐	16. helps build my self-confidence			☐ ☐ ☐
☐ ☐ ☐	17. helps me become responsible for myself			☐ ☐ ☐
☐ ☐ ☐	18. has created good childhood memories for me			☐ ☐ ☐

- In which of these areas do your parents deserve a pat on the back?

☞ In which of these areas do your parents need improvement?

☞ How can you cooperate with their efforts to improve?

(Adapted from the Hoover-Bedley Parenting Perception Scale in *The Big R* by GENE BEDLEY)

Simple Tips for Growing Good Kids

☞ Parents, let your kids tell you at least one way to do something meaningful for them in each of these areas.

Love them

Listen to them

Limit their experiments,
      but never their horizons

Learn from them

Laugh with them

Lavish them with praise

Lead them in your faith

Light the path ahead of them

Let them go

Drawing Closer

☞ To work together in building up each family member's feeling of importance, decide together on ways you can encourage each other. Write each family member's initials in one of the circles below, and inside the box tell something you can do (1) to make him or her know your love, and (2) to nurture your friendship with him or her.

(1)   (2)

(1)   (2)

(1)   (2)

(1)   (2)

(1)   (2)

(1)   (2)

IN OUR FAMILY, eating dinner together is:
- ☐ an important ritual
- ☐ something we'd like to do if we had time
- ☐ important, but we watch TV while we eat
- ☐ unimportant

Important rituals in our family life that draw us closer are…

In our family, working or playing together in our free time is:
- ☐ something we strive for
- ☐ something we rarely have time for
- ☐ less important than getting things accomplished individually
- ☐ something we do, but it just happens

The things we try to do together regularly are…

Enhancing Relationships

Go around the family circle and take turns describing each person's relationship with every other family member. Each of you can complete these sentences:

- I would describe my current relationship with…(name of each family member) as…
- I would like our relationship to be like…
- I want our relationship to grow in these ways…

☞ We can make this happen by…

(Use this chart to note each person's comments. To make it ready, record each person's initials in *both* the left-hand column and across the top row.)

	◯	◯	◯	◯	◯
◯					
◯					
◯					
◯					
◯					

Character Models

PARENTS,

What qualities do you want to model for your daughter(s)?

☞ What could you do together to show you appreciate her femininity?

What qualities do you want to model for your son(s)?

☞ What could you do together to show you appreciate his masculinity?

Ask your daughters and sons to give you feedback.

Family Atmosphere

- Use five adjectives to describe the emotional atmosphere in your home.

- Use five adjectives to describe the kind of atmosphere you would like to prevail at home.

☞ List at least five ways you can create this atmosphere, or are maintaining the atmosphere you desire in your home.

- Have each family member tell about your favorite family activity that's free.
  Why is it your favorite?
  ☐ Singing together ☐ Wrestling on the floor ☐ Popcorn and pillow fights
  ☐ Sleeping under the stars ☐ Taking walks ☐ Other activities:

- What form of entertainment does your family regularly enjoy?
  ☐ Movies ☐ Sports ☐ Crafts ☐ Games ☐ TV and videos
  ☐ Camping ☐ Eating out ☐ Trips and sightseeing ☐ Other

- What forms of entertainment are best at helping your family relax?

- Which of these best help you to stay in touch with each other?

- Do any of these prevent you from interacting with one another?
  Which ones?

- Which of these are the most fun for everybody?

- What kinds of entertainment facilitate interaction
  and help create good memories for your family?

Evaluating Stress & Crisis

TO BE REAL OR TO BE CAREFULLY KEPT?

"What is REAL?" asked the Rabbit one day. "Does it mean having things that buzz inside you and a stick-out handle?"

"Real isn't how you are made," said the Skin Horse. "It's a thing that happens to you. When a child loves you for a long, long time, not just to play with, but REALLY loves you, then you become Real."

"Does it hurt?"

"Sometimes." For he was always truthful. "When you are Real you don't mind being hurt."

"Does it happen all at once, like being wound up, or bit by bit?"

"It doesn't happen all at once. You become. It takes a long time. That's why it doesn't often happen to people who break easily, or who have sharp edges, or who have to be carefully kept. Generally, by the time you are Real, most of your hair has been loved off, and your eyes drop out and you get loose in the joints and very shabby.

"But these things don't matter at all, because once you are Real you can't be ugly, except to people who don't understand."

MARGERY WILLIAMS, *The Velveteen Rabbit*

* * *

WHEN STRESSFUL CONDITIONS trigger a chain of emotional reactions in my family, I know it is time for us to reaffirm our commitment to each other, to monitor sources of stress, eliminate them wherever possible, and learn from those we cannot change that process is more important than achievement and position.

Rick Linamen, father of two, and experienced family counselor in Scottsdale, Arizona, points out that the tendency within our culture is toward bottom-line thinking.

"The end result is all important to people," he states. "We're geared to goals and projects. We are driven to do, to achieve and accomplish. But every counseling principle that I know of stresses the significance of the process itself."

It is what we learn through crises that creates growth of character and stretches the muscles of our souls, making us strong. Family crises are often preceded by discomforting symptoms that should be recognized for what they are. Danger signals tip us off to the fact that we need to make some changes, changes that will lead to further growth, if we let them.

For the modern family, some of these symptoms seem universal:

- calendars filled with appointments for individual activities
- communication between marriage partners channeled indirectly through the children or limited to practical necessities
- changing homes, remodeling, refurnishing, and then moving again
- infrequent sexual contact between partners
- the "system" consistently wins; over-

time and extra work become normal
- increasingly frequent arguments and disagreements between siblings
- time together means only watching TV
- constant criticism and self-justification; no one wants to say "I'm sorry"

Crises precipitated by these symptoms can be managed if we start early and give ourselves regular checkups. Reassessment of personal values can be a great aid. Professional counsel is invaluable.

But the flow of family life is never predictable. Crises are never one-hundred percent avoidable. We all will experience heated emotions, unexpected disruptions, and heartaches. The potential for spontaneous combustion is part of what life's all about.

Hopefully, the exercise of family life will develop within each one of us patience, common sense, and strength to help each other. Hopefully, the stress we are unable to change will wear us smooth, make us mellow, and keep us real. Perhaps, the crises themselves will authenticate our lives.

Personal Family Assessment

If you were asked to assess the degree of impact that the Christmas season had on your ability to recover from a confrontation with a friend or relative, would you be able to do it? The tests in this section have been included to enable your family to identify and attach a measurable quantity to the stressors in your lives. Utilizing these will alert you to any danger of stress overload, and perhaps help you and your children to understand each other better by understanding the stress points in your lives.

Compare your individual scores on the following tests. Assess the sources of family crisis and use your test results as a springboard for discussion.

Evaluating Stress

Each item in the list on the next page has a score associated with it. Check those items that pertain to you within the past year, then add up your score.

The higher your score, the more stress you are experiencing. If your score is 30 or less, your stress ratio is minimum. If your score is between 30 and 90, you are experiencing moderate stress. If your score is above 90 your stress ration is serious.

- What areas of stress in each of your lives could be eliminated?

- What areas of stress can be minimized by communication and mutual support?

☞ In what specific ways can you structure a pattern of communication and support that is satisfactory to both of you?

☞ What have you learned about your spouse's needs and your own needs from studying the test results?

Holmes and Rahe
Stress Scale for Adults

Event:	Scale:	SCORES: His	Hers	Event:	Scale:	SCORES: His	Hers
1. Marriage	50	___	___	28. Major change in the number of arguments with spouse	35	___	___
2. Troubles with the boss	23	___	___	29. Major changes in responsibilities at work (promotion, demotion,transfer)	29	___	___
3. Detention in jail or other institution	63			30. Wife beginning or ceasing work outside the home	26	___	___
4. Death of spouse	100	___	___	31. Major change in working hours or conditions	20	___	___
5. Major change in sleeping habits	16	___	___	32. Major change in type and/or amount of recreation	19	___	___
6. Death of a close family member	63	___	___	33. Taking on a mortgage greater than $10,000	31	___	___
7. Major change in eating habits	15	___	___	34. Taking on a mortgage or loan less than $10,000	17	___	___
8. Foreclosure on a mortgage or loan	30	___	___	35. Major personal injury or illness	53	___	___
9. Revision of personal habits	24	___	___	36. Major business readjustment (merger, reorganization, bankruptcy, etc.)	39	___	___
10. Death of a close friend	37	___	___	37. Major change in social activities	18	___	___
11. Minor violations of the law (traffic tickets, etc.)	11	___	___	38. Major change in material living conditions	25	___	___
12. Outstanding personal achievement	28	___	___	39. Retirement from work	45	___	___
13. Pregnancy	40	___	___	40. Vacation	13	___	___
14. Major change in the health of a family member	44	___	___	41. Christmas	12	___	___
15. Sexual difficulties	39	___	___	42. Changing to a new school	20	___	___
16. In-Law troubles	29	___	___	43. Beginning or ceasing formal schooling	26	___	___
17. Major change in number of family get-togethers	15	___	___				
18. Major change in financial state	38	___	___	TOTAL SCORES:		___	___
19. Gaining a new family member	39	___	___				
20. Change in residence	20	___	___				
21. Son or daughter leaving house (marriage, college)	29	___	___				
22. Marital separation	65	___	___				
23. Major change in church activities	19	___	___				
24. Marital reconciliation	45	___	___				
25. Being fired from work	47	___	___				
26. Divorce	73	___	___				
27. Changing to a different line of work	36	___	___				

(Social Readjustment Rating Questionnaire from Journal of Psychosomatic Research: Volume 11, 1967)

Stress Test for Kids

Have each child complete the stress test on the opposite page, scoring answers in the column under his or her initials.

- What areas of stress could be eliminated in each child's life?

☞ In what ways can you support your child if he or she is under pressures that cannot be eliminated?

- What can you learn about each child from his or her test results?

STRESS TEST FOR KIDS

your initials:

	EVENT:	Score:	[ ]	[ ]	[ ]
1	Parent dies	100			
2	Parents divorce	73			
3	Parents separate	65			
4	Parent travels as part of job	63			
5	Close family member dies	63			
6	Personal illness or injury	53			
7	Parent remarries	50			
8	Parent fired from job	47			
9	Parents reconcile	45			
10	Mother beginning outside work	45			
11	Change in health of family member	44			
12	Mother becomes pregnant	40			
13	School difficulties	39			
14	Birth of a sibling	39			
15	Major change at same school	39			
16	Change in family's financial condition	38			
17	Injury or illness of a close friend	37			
18	Starts new freetime activity	36			
19	Change in number of fights with siblings	35			
20	Threatened by violence	31			
21	Theft of personal possessions	30			
22	Changes in type or number of responsibilities	29			
23	Older sibling leaves home	29			
24	Trouble with grandparents	29			
25	Outstanding personal achievement	28			
26	Moves to another location	26			
27	Moves to another part of town	26			
28	Receives or loses a pet	25			
29	Changes personal habits	24			
30	Trouble with teacher	24			
31	Change of hours in child care	20			
32	Moves to a new house	20			
33	Starts at a new school	20			
34	Changes play habits	19			
35	Vacations with family	19			
36	Changes friends	18			
37	Attends summer camp	17			
38	Changes sleeping habits	16			
39	Change in number of family get-togethers	15			
40	Changes eating habits	15			
41	Changes amount of TV viewing	13			
42	Celebrates birthday	12			
	TOTALS:				

STRESS TEST FOR KIDS (from *Stress in the Family* by Tim Timmons)

Family Crisis

- What are three or four primary sources of recurring crises in your family unit?
  - ☐ overlapping responsibilities   ☐ money   ☐ in-laws   ☐ health
  - ☐ school   ☐ personal belongings   ☐ career   ☐ leisure activities
  - ☐ lack of leisure   ☐ communication snags   ☐ drugs/alcohol
  - ☐ other sources:

- How have these been handled positively in the past? What went right for you then?

- What are some ways to neutralize stressful emotions before crises occur? (*Possible ideas:* [1] Meet the basic need behind them such as food, rest, exercise; [2] be aware of the trigger effect, and determine to respond instead of react.)

- Who will be responsible for alerting your family to danger signals, and when?

☞ How can you make crises work for you instead of against you? (*Possible ideas:* [1] Talk about what happened after emotions have subsided; [2] attack the problem, not the people; [3] identify the purpose of working through this particular crisis.)

☞ What truths have you learned about each other through past crises? (*Some examples:* •Mom has a need to talk about personal things with Dad; •Little sister finds it hard to apologize; needs role models in this area; •Dad needs more time for hobbies and relaxation; •Brother needs our support in school work.)

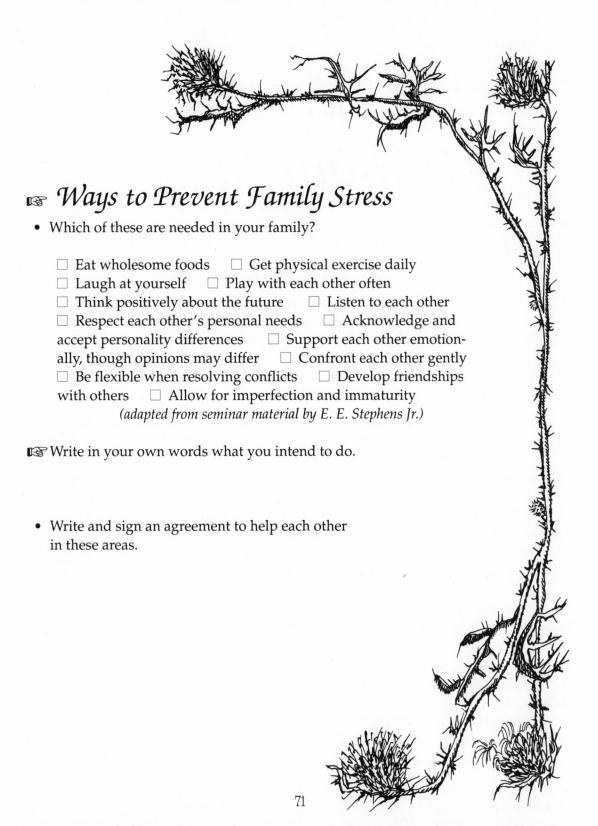

☞ *Ways to Prevent Family Stress*

• Which of these are needed in your family?

☐ Eat wholesome foods ☐ Get physical exercise daily
☐ Laugh at yourself ☐ Play with each other often
☐ Think positively about the future ☐ Listen to each other
☐ Respect each other's personal needs ☐ Acknowledge and
accept personality differences ☐ Support each other emotionally, though opinions may differ ☐ Confront each other gently
☐ Be flexible when resolving conflicts ☐ Develop friendships
with others ☐ Allow for imperfection and immaturity
(adapted from seminar material by E. E. Stephens Jr.)

☞ Write in your own words what you intend to do.

• Write and sign an agreement to help each other
in these areas.

Communicating Commitment

OF COMMITMENT AND CONFLICT

If Camille and I can just stay together another twenty-five years, then we also will have reached the Twilight Zone, where one of us will do something idiotic and the other one not only will understand it but admire it as well.

You turned out the light where I'm reading, I will tell her. *Thank you for the surprise trip to the planetarium.*

You left your shoes in the bathtub, she will tell me. *Thank you for giving me two more boats.*

BILL COSBY, *Love and Marriage*

OUR HOMES are environments with their own fine-tuned ecological balance. A home becomes a source of affirmation and personal growth when we talk about felt needs, speak truthfully about the facts, and accept one another's foibles as neutral ground. Confrontations in a humorous vein certainly don't hurt and can be developed, taking the sting out of conflict.

But hurts do happen in my home. Disappointments are not that rare. Sometimes, the proliferation of conflicts becomes a tangled web. We all need practice in learning to discern the differ-ence between little issues and big issues, saving our steam for the big things and neutralizing the small ones by seeing them through forgiving eyes. E. E. Stephens comments, "This takes creative thinking and a determination not to react. We react when we are hungry, tired, hurt, rushed, or feeling over-whelmed. When we allow ourselves to react, we can't see our way out of diffi-culty and frequently make it worse."

When we do react, emotions make major issues of minor ones. And resolv-ing major conflicts requires much more work: a concentrated effort to deal with facts and feelings, and to establish a goal for the future of the relationship.

Children are continually absorbing information about conflict resolution. They are learning to deal with personal conflicts the way their parents do. Clara Schuster, Child and Family Development Specialist at Kent State University stresses the need for children to see themselves as people in process and to see their parents as people in process, too. "We are all in this together," she states. "We need to see and deal with our humanness, to break down communication barriers. That does not mean that parents lose face or their children's respect. Neither does it mean that children have equal power in decision making. It means that we see each other as people worthy of respect, doing our best in this journey of life."

One thing is certain: With all the bumps and bruises ahead of us, the way we respond to family conflicts will either reveal the depth of our commitment to each other or expose its limitations.

In *The Art of Loving*, Erich Fromm wrote: "Just as it is customary for people to believe that pain and sadness should be avoided under all circumstances, they believe that love means the absence of any conflict.... Real conflicts between people...are not destructive. They lead to clarification, they produce a catharsis from which both persons emerge with more knowledge and more strength."

Personal Family Assessment

A story is told of Michelangelo rolling a huge stone down the street when someone stopped and asked, "What are you doing with that?"

The master sculptor is said to have replied, without looking up, "There's an angel in this stone, and I'm going to find it."

The exercises in this chapter are designed to help you discover the angel in your stone.

☞ *The Way We Were/ The Way We Are*

How often have you recalled the feelings with which you came into marriage? Whatever happened to those feelings? Have you updated your commitment to each other, including working through the tough times, by refocusing your expectations and reestablishing your purpose? As you answer the questions below, perhaps you can come up with a few more to ask each other.

- What were your expectations when you married?

- How is your marriage measuring up to those expectations?

- In which of these areas are you experiencing the most conflict?

- Where have you made (or are you willing to make) compromises in order to bring more harmony into your relationship?

- Is there a particular area in your marriage where it might be good to seek professional counseling?

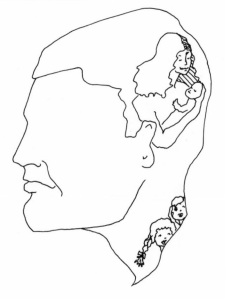

Talking About Our Kids:

- What are the primary conflicts that arise between you and your children? Between your children?

- What methods of discipline are most effective for each child?
    ☐ restrictions   ☐ time outs   ☐ denial of privileges, including allowances
    ☐ spankings   ☐ other methods:

- What special privilege would be most effective to offer your children as an encouragement or reward?

- What guidelines should you set for these areas of potential conflict in your family?
    ☐ money   ☐ telephone   ☐ friends over/going out   ☐ curfews/bedtimes
    ☐ after school activities/scheduling   ☐ other areas:

- Would it be helpful to meet regularly to discuss your family conflicts? To discuss emotional issues? When is the best time to meet?

- When is the best time to iron out details and schedules for the day?
    ☐ in the morning   ☐ the night before   ☐ some other time:

Are You Giving Your Children...

- too much freedom, which can result in a lack of discipline and moral guidance;
- too many material goods as a substitute for the time you should be spending with them;
- too much pressure to perform, with resulting stress that may cause your children to cave in and underachieve;
- too much information and too little instruction about how to use that information maturely;
- too much protection, with too little preparation for the difficult challenges of the real world;
- too much independence, accompanied by too little practical advice about how to deal with the pains of growing up;
- too much food and too little advice about good nutrition;
- too much parental sacrifice, with too little education at home about the basic responsibilities of life.

(From *Kids Who Have Too Much,* by Dr. Ralph E Minear and William Proctor)

Take two or three of these and decide how you will replace the "too much" with a corresponding quality that is good for your child.

About Feelings

In the box marked with your initials, complete each of these ten sentences:

1. It makes me upset when…   **2.** It makes me happy when…   **3.** I get embarrassed when…   **4.** I feel proud to be part of this family when…   **5.** Something I wish my family would do more often is…   **6.** It makes me feel helpless when…   **7.** I wish somebody would ask me about my…   **8.** The biggest disagreements between me and my parents are…   **9.** I would like to see a smoother relationship between me and my brothers and sisters in the area of…   **10.** In these areas, I am willing to make these compromises:

✍ Families with High Self Esteem

- Which of the following are true in your family?

  ☐ acceptance of each other's feelings   ☐ spirit of cooperation   ☐ permission to be different from other family members   ☐ clearly defined and established limits   ☐ frequent communication   ☐ assertive and responsible behavior

- In which of these areas do you need improvement?

- How can you make steps toward improvement?

Some Hot Topics

- What attitudes about sexuality are you nourishing in your family?

- Are you able to talk openly and honestly about sexual issues, using real words?

- What are your personal family morals and beliefs, the kind of things you want your children and friends to understand?

- How important a part of your daily life is TV?

- What is your primary purpose for owning a TV? Is it being fulfilled?

- Is TV a source of any major or minor conflicts?

- What can help you solve these conflicts?

- What choice things has TV allowed you to be a part of in the past?

  ☐ Presidental elections   ☐ The first moon walk   ☐ The Olympics   ☐ Others?

- What choice things would you like to see in the future?

When You Get Mad...
What Kind of Animal Are You?

"Each of us has a particular style of conflict....A skunk makes a big stink about everything...not satisfied until he has raised his tail and squirted stink-juice over every issue....

"The shark moves in for the kill....The person who fights like a Shark is known for his or her sharp tongue. Verbal abuse (and sometimes physical abuse as well) is the Shark's trademark, and once the Shark gets started, it is not long before he has whipped himself into a frenzy...

"Few animals have natural protection as excellent as that of the turtle, which is the world's only reptile with a shell. And of the 240 species of turtles, not a one of them has a vocal cord. The turtle has no true voice....Consequently we find the Turtle expressing his opinion in subtle, passive-aggressive ways....

"A master of disguise — that's the Chameleon...vulnerable to the attacks of numerous enemies...they avoid fighting by distorting the facts. On and on goes the Chameleon, excusing himself by blaming others, putting on the mask of innocence, distorting the facts of his own misdeeds."

(WILL CUNNINGHAM, *How to Enjoy a Family Fight*)

In conflict styles, what kind of "animal" is each member of your family?

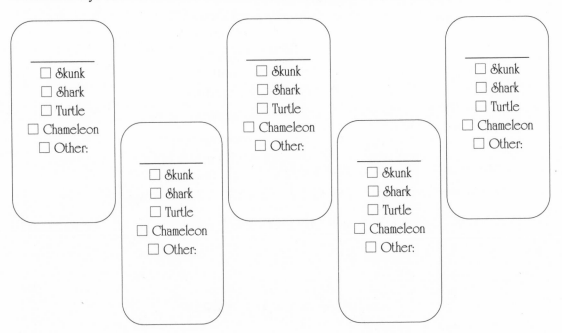

Hints for Conflict Resolution: "How Are We Doing?"

- Define a critical issue between two members of the family.

- Determine when the problem actually began

- Practice the Five-Plus-Five Rule:
One person gets five minutes to state his perspective while the other listens. The second person paraphrases this perspective back to the first person to his satisfaction. Now, the second person gets five minutes to state his perspective, which is then paraphrased by the first person.

- Stay in touch with reality: Ask, What am I feeling now? (angry, weary, hungry, hurt, alone?) What is the real reason for my feeling this way? (Is it a delayed reaction to something that happened hours ago, yesterday, last week?) Who are my feelings directed at? (Am I displacing my anger onto a more vulnerable, but innocent person?)

- Determine: Is this issue a real conflict of interests or is it only a misunderstanding?

- If it is a real conflict, how important is it?

- If the conflict is at a standoff, use creative problem-solving techniques (See chapter 12) to deal with it.

(Adapted from seminar material by E. E. STEPHENS JR.)

One Family's Approach
to Resolving a Conflict

The following illustration will give you an idea of how
creating a structure around a conflict and the persons
involved in the conflict will provide a way to resolve
the real issues and release emotional turmoil.

A THIRTEEN-YEAR-OLD GIRL we'll call Anne broke the trust of her parents and
went beyond the limits of her parents' guidelines by becoming sexually active. Her
parents panicked, laying down the law that she would not be permitted to date until
age eighteen.

Anne became angry and withdrawn. After consulting with a professional, her parents identified the key issues and drew up a plan through which their daughter could
earn back their trust. Guided by the counselor, Anne and her parents developed a
three-year system to facilitate this.

For the first six months, Anne would be allowed to group date as long as her parents provided the transportation and knew the kids going along. During the next six
months, Anne would be allowed to group date, with the parents of her friends providing transportation as long as her parents knew who would be going. Over the following six months she would be allowed to double date as long as her parents provided
the transportation. In the next six months Anne would be allowed to double date with
the parent of a friend driving.

If Anne proved worthy of their trust up to that point, then in the last year in the
three-year system she would be allowed to go on single dates — with her parents providing the transportation the first six months, and another adult providing the transportation the last six months. The goal was to allow Anne to single-date at age sixteen.

This system gave Anne a reachable goal to look forward to, and an opportunity to
win back her parents' trust. The system gave Anne's parents a period of time to communicate the reasons behind the limits they set and to prove to Anne that their limits
were set in love and concern.

(Adapted from seminar material by E. E. STEPHENS JR.)

Making the Most of What We've Got

Managing Our Money

THINGS WILL NEVER BE PERFECT

Can you really "have it all now"? Judging from TV and the movies, Superwoman is alive and well. You know the one, the fashionably dressed, perfectly made-up mother of four who runs a million-dollar business in her spare time. That is, when she's not lecturing at Harvard, advising Congress on how to avert national disaster or appearing on a TV talk show to tell us all how to use our food processors during natural childbirth. Of course, she wouldn't think of letting her husband help with the housework.

Well, there is no such woman. Thank goodness! You cannot have everything, do everything, and be everything, all at the same time.... Maintaining a strong marriage, happy and healthy kids, and a career you enjoy are realistic goals as long as you keep in mind that things will never be perfect.

BINGHAM, EDMONDSON, & STRYKER, *Choices*

I CAN ADMIT that my own personal dreams may never be fulfilled. But it is difficult for me to accept the notion that my kids may not live up to the dreams conceived for them long before they were conceived. And I sense this same tendency in other parents who, in a determination to give kids a head start, hurry them along from infancy, shuffling sons and daughters from swimming to soccer to computer tutoring, compressing their childhood into intense segments of developmental education. This tendency became clear to me recently when my sixth grade daughter came home from school with a brochure for a kid's career seminar in *Stocks, Bonds, and More!*

Challenges in the adult marketplace alongside a wealth of information geared to improve our performance as parents would seem to work against each other, but they feed on the same kind of ambitions. Along with demands to achieve higher levels in our careers, we parents feel pressured to live up to Supermom and Superdad images, raising high performance kids.

In *Newsweek* magazine's special edition on "The 21st Century Family" (Winter-Spring 1990), Dr. Benjamin Spock stated: "Parents should raise their kids not primarily to get ahead but to serve, to cooperate, to be kind. By far the most disturbing force in America today, to my mind, is excessive competitiveness. It keeps people obsessed with their jobs and with personal advancement. It encourages parents to downgrade the family. Instead we should raise our children to feel that family ties are the most rewarding values; that social, cultural and community activities can be deeply satisfying, and that the gratification from income and prestige in a majority of jobs these days is shallow by comparison."

We know we can never go back to the post-World War II era when families sat on their front porch summer evenings just watching fireflies. Today there are too many channels and too many choices and too much to do to get ahead for the next day, and the next (and, maybe if we hurry, we can earn enough to buy a boat for our summer vacations). But we sometimes wish we had a front porch.

My family has found that we need to loosen up and slow down, taking our purpose seriously — but, as the saying goes, not ourselves. We've decided to capitalize on the qualities that make us unique and refuse to compare ourselves with others. What works for other families may not work for us anyway. We've decided to define what we want, then explore our own potential before we gallop headlong into someone else's story.

Perhaps we'll slow down long enough to sit in the twilight and catch a few fireflies. Perhaps we'll experience for ourselves the truth in what the British theologian C. H. Spurgeon once said: "It is not how much we have, but how much we enjoy that makes happiness."

Do Our Savings and Spending Reflect Our Values?

HIS:		HERS:

How would I describe our personal values as reflected by the way we handle money?

How much of our total monthly income do I think would be appropriate to save?

What is my highest priority for the money we save?

How much do I think should be allocated for spending per month?

Beyond essentials, what are my priorities for spending?

☐ entertainment/recreation ☐ hobbies
☐ home improvement ☐ classes and lessons
☐ clothes and personal items ☐ gifts
☐ other areas:

☐ entertainment/recreation ☐ hobbies
☐ home improvement ☐ classes and lessons
☐ clothes and personal items ☐ gifts
☐ other areas:

In what areas would I like to have more to spend?

Where can cuts be made in order to have more to save or spend in other areas?

How could we generate more income for our family?

Financial Statement

WHAT YOU OWN:

CASH:

Cash on hand	$ _____
Checking accounts	_____
Savings accounts	_____
Money-market funds	_____
Life insurance cash value	_____
Money owed you	_____
Other	_____

MARKETABLE SECURITIES:

Stocks	$ _____
Bonds	_____
Government securities	_____
Mutual funds	_____
Other investments	_____

PERSONAL PROPERTY:

Automobiles	$ _____
Household furnishings	_____
Art, antiques, other collectibles	_____
Clothing, furs	_____
Jewelry	_____
Other possessions	_____

REAL ESTATE:

Homes	$ _____
Other properties	_____

PENSION:

Vested portion of company plan	$ _____
Vested benefits	_____
IRA	_____
Keogh	_____

LONG-TERM ASSETS:

Equity in business	$ _____
Life Insurance	_____
Annuities	_____

TOTAL: $ _____

WHAT YOU OWE:

CURRENT BILLS:

Rent	$ _____
Utilities	_____
Charge accounts	_____
Credit cards	_____
Insurance premiums	_____
Alimony	_____
Child support	_____
Other bills	_____
	_____
	_____

TAXES:

Federal	$ _____
State	_____
Local	_____
Taxes on investments	_____
Other	_____

MORTGAGES:

Homes	$ _____
Other Properties	_____

DEBTS TO INDIVIDUALS: $ _____

LOANS:

Auto	$ _____
Education	_____
Home improvement	_____
Life insurance	_____
Other	_____
	_____

TOTAL $ _____

What you own
minus what you owe
equals your **NET WORTH:** $ _____

12-Month Budget

ANNUAL INCOME:

Salary	$ _____
Bonus	_____
Dividends	_____
Interest	_____
Proceeds from sale of securities	_____
Rental income	_____
Trust income	_____
Social security	_____
Pension	_____
Alimony	_____
Child support	_____
Unemployment, Disability insurance	_____
Other income	_____
TOTAL INCOME:	$ _____

FIXED EXPENSES:

Mortgage rent	$ _____
Fuel	_____
Electricity	_____
Telephone	_____
Water	_____
Personal property taxes	_____
Real estate taxes	_____
Homeowner insurance premium	_____
Automobile insurance premium	_____
Medical disability insurance premium	_____
Life insurance premium	_____
Automobile loan	_____
Loan or installment debt repayment	_____
Other	_____
TOTAL FIXED EXPENSES	$ _____

FLEXIBLE EXPENSES:

Food and beverage	$ _____
Clothing	_____
Laundry and cleaning	_____
Personal care	_____
Entertainment	_____
Travel and vacation	_____
Recreation	_____
Gifts	_____
Household help	_____
Repairs	_____
Home furnishings	_____
Appliance purchases	_____
Gasoline	_____
Communication	_____
Health care	_____
Child care	_____
Education	_____
Gifts and donations	_____
Investments	_____
Savings	_____
Personal allowance	_____
Other	_____
TOTAL FLEXIBLE EXPENSES	$ _____
TOTAL EXPENSES	$ _____

What About Our Children's Financial Needs?

- What is the most important thing you want your children to learn about money?

- What is your plan for teaching your children this?

- Have you and your spouse agreed upon guidelines for your children's use of their allowance? What are these guidelines?

- Does your child have a savings account? What is his/her objective for the account?

- Have you considered pledging a portion of total cost of your child's financial objective if he/she earns and saves the rest?

- When or upon what basis should your children's allowance be increased (or decreased)?

- What kind of education do you want your children to have?

- What is the estimated cost? (See next page.)

- How much money do you estimate you will be able to provide toward this? Are you on schedule?

- What are the most advantageous ways for you to save/invest for your children's education? Why?

WHAT TO SAVE FOR COLLEGE

Here's what you might pay for four years of college when your child reaches 18. To calculate how much money you have to save: (1) Go to the line closest to your child's age. (2) Multiply your current college savings fund by the Savings Factor, to see what it might be worth in the future. (3) Subtract the result from the price of four years of education and divide by the Investment Factor. That's how much to save each month, assuming you earn 8 percent annually on the money.

Child's age	Public college*	Private college*	Savings Factor	Investment Factor
3	$80,188	$153,259	3.17	348.35
6	$65,457	$125,105	2.52	242.11
9	$53,433	$102,123	2.00	158.48
12	$43,617	$83,363	1.59	92.64
15	$35,604	$68,049	1.26	40.81

*college inflation rate figured at 7%

Source: T. Rowe Price (*Newsweek*, Winter 1990)

DON'T LET these figures scare you. Use them as a springboard to start thinking about the realistic possibilities for educating your children. You may want to discuss job opportunities with your kids assuming they get a college education, and job opportunities assuming they do not get a college education. You also may want to discuss conceivable ways to make their future education a family project starting today.

What About Our Home?

- If buying a home, when will your mortgage be paid off?

- Could you possibly put more toward the principal so it could be paid off sooner?

- If renting, are you interested in buying a home someday?

- How much have you saved toward a down payment?

- What is your estimated date of purchase?

What About Financial Protection?

- Is your life and/or disability insurance coverage enough to cover your predicted needs in event of loss of income due to sickness or death?

- If not, how much money per month could you put into increasing your coverage?

- Are there any cash values in your life insurance? How much at present?

- What will the cash values be at your estimated age of retirement if you do not borrow or use them beforehand?

- For what would you want your spouse to use the life insurance money in the event of your death?

What About Retirement?

- At what age(s) do you expect to retire?

- Where will your retirement income come from?
  - ☐ Social Security? How much per month?
  - ☐ Pension? How much per month?
  - ☐ Private savings? How much per month?

- Are your Social Security tax records up-to-date and correct? When have you last had them verified and corrected, if necessary? (Contact your local Social Security office for verification forms.)

- How much are you currently investing annually in a tax deferred retirement plan? How much more could you invest in it per year, taking into consideration the tax savings you would benefit from?

WHAT TO SAVE FOR RETIREMENT

To live a comfortable, nonworking life, you'll need at least 75 percent of your pre-retirement income. Part of that money will come from social security and maybe a pension. For the rest, you'll have to save. Here's what a typical working couple should be putting aside each year, assuming 5 percent wage inflation and retirement at the age of 65.

| | | Needed to invest annually*: | |
Current salary	Current age	With a company pension	With a double IRA but no pension**
$35,000	30	$3,660	$4,000
	40	$4,360	$5,990
	50	$6,000	$9,970
$50,000	30	$7,590	$8,350
	40	$8,940	$11,790
	50	$12,280	$17,950
$75,000	30	$15,270	$18,050
	40	$17,890	$23,220
	50	$24,730	$33,700

*At 8 percent, taxed in a state and federal bracket of 35 percent
**including $4,000 for the IRAs

Source: Ernst and Young (*Newsweek*, Winter 1990)

✍ How Much is Enough?

Write the answers to the following questions in your notebooks as they are read aloud.
Then discuss your answers with your parents.

- How important to you is money?
- What attitudes have you picked up from your parents about money?
- How important to you is it to be free to decide how to spend or save your own money — your allowance and the money you earn?
- Do you have a plan for saving and spending? What percent of your allowance do you save? What percent do you spend?
- Do you think it is important for kids to have their own savings account? What about kids owning a credit card?
- What do you usually spend your allowance on?
- If you are saving any of it, what are you saving for?
- Do you think your allowance is adequate?
- What reasons would you give your mom and dad for wanting to receive more allowance?

- What are some creative ways you could earn extra money?
  - ☐ babysitting
  - ☐ party helper/decorator
  - ☐ errand runner for senior citizens
  - ☐ dog walking/pet care
  - ☐ organizing garage sales
  - ☐ newspaper routes
  - ☐ yardwork
  - ☐ sales
  - ☐ other ideas

- What kind of education or training would you like to get after high school?
- How much do you think it will cost?
- How much could you save toward this cost?
- When do you want to start saving toward this?

Just For Fun

Do your kids know where your income comes from and where it goes?

Use this circle to make a family money pie. Specify on the outside of the circle where your income comes from; what you do to earn it, how many hours are involved. Divide the pie into sections (let the younger children color them) showing what percent of monthly income goes to what expenses in your family. If there is a sliver left over, discuss why or what you should save it for:

☐ family vacations ☐ set up an account for homeless families
☐ home improvement ☐ travel to faraway places ☐ _____

...or what you should spend it on:

☐ high quality food ☐ movies, books ☐ give to friends in need
☐ household necessities ☐ _____ ☐ _____

- Talk about how your family can have fun even if you spend very little money.

    1. Capitalize on the variety in seasons and beauty of nature by going hiking, sledding, camping, ice fishing.

    2. Do cozy indoor parties with simple themes, paper decorations, old-fashioned song fests.

    3. Create your own games with household items such as a box of tiny crackers, pennies, buttons, or string.

    Others:
    4.

    5.

- If you could earn a million dollars, how would you...

    1. like to earn it?

    2. help your family?

    3. treat yourself?

    4. help others?

- If you were to lose your home and possessions tomorrow...

    1. What would you miss the most?

    2. What wouldn't you miss very much?

    3. In what ways would you still be happy and thankful?

Stoking
the Home Fires

THE TIME WE WASTE

The little prince went away, to look again at the roses.

"You are not at all like my rose," he said. "...she is more important than all the hundreds of you other roses: because it is she that I have watered; because it is she that I have put under the glass globe; because it is she that I have sheltered behind the screen; because it is for her that I have killed the caterpillars (except the two or three that we saved to become butterflies); because it is she that I have listened to, when she grumbled, or boasted, or even sometimes when she said nothing. Because she is my rose.

"It is the time you have wasted for your rose that makes your rose so important."

ANTOINE DE SAINT-EXUPERY, *The Little Prince*

* * *

EACH MEMBER of a household is a *homemaker* by token of living in a home with others and belonging to a family. The ancient world's wisest king, King Solomon, wrote in the Bible, "By wisdom a house is built, and through understanding it is established; through knowledge its rooms are filled with rare and beautiful treasures."

Though the responsibility for maintaining an orderly and imaginative atmosphere at home has, in our culture, been most often dependent upon Mom's understanding, Dad is taking new cues and adapting to new roles in keeping the home fires burning.

There are still men who pride themselves on reminding the ladies how *important* homemaking is. But when my own husband got his hands wet cleaning the toilet bowl, started doing the laundry on weekends, and took the initiative to put flowers on the dinner table, turn the music on and dance the toddler to sleep, he proved that he truly valued the years I had invested in work at home.

Children are homemakers, too. Kids instinctively sense the difference between a token chore and the real thing. Knowing they're needed creates a vital change of attitude. When their contribution to a happy, tidy home is valued and enforced, their spirits soar.

One mother commented, "I'm trying to teach my kids how to make good meals and good memories. At our house even cleaning and cooking have to be done in the context of creating an atmosphere to remember fondly." This woman was convinced that giving her children a happy childhood would be determined not so much by special privileges or special occasions, but by the vivid impact of everyday experiences upon their senses.

For children, repetitive routines can become great memories when they are combined with emotive sounds, smells, tastes and touches: setting the breakfast table each morning to one of Mozart's sonatas, bathing each Saturday with a certain perfumed soap, enjoying pumpkin-nut cookies while raking leaves each fall, a comforting back rub at the end of bad days. Whether we are making memories or making beds, homemaking should not be defined by the things that have to be done, but by the imagination with which we do them.

Personal Family Assessment

There is both a practical and a personal side to keeping the home. As King Solomon observed, the job takes fair measures of wisdom, understanding, and knowledge. For some families, this chapter may require new ways of thinking about the organization of housework. Please go into this with a positive attitude and an open mind so that homemaking can become a fulfilling part of family life for everyone.

Talk About Roles

Answer the following questions in your notebooks. Exchange answers and read them, then take ten minutes to discuss them and take notes below.

- What homekeeping responsibilities do you want your spouse to help you with?

- What housekeeping jobs do you think you should be doing?

- What jobs do you want to be responsible for?

☞ Would you be willing to exchange certain roles with your spouse for a period of time in order to learn how to do them, and to learn more about each other?

- How do you feel about the way you are currently functioning in your housekeeping roles?

☞ If you could change something, what would that be?

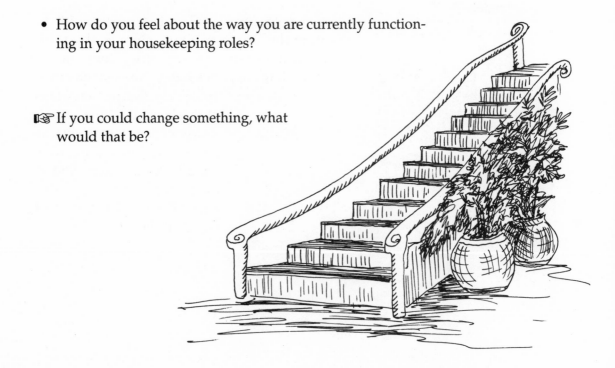

Steps to Keeping the Home

Read this list aloud, then record below each family member's initials as he or she votes— *favorite jobs, jobs I don't mind, and jobs I dislike* — for each job category mentioned listed. Evaluate each person's capabilities to do an effective job in each area.

	Favorite Jobs	Don't Mind	Dislike
MEALS			
Planning meals			
Preparing meals			
Grocery shopping			
Cleaning up after meals			
HOUSECLEANING			
Vacuuming			
Cleaning floors			
Picking up clutter			
Washing windows			
Cleaning bedroom			
Dusting, polishing furniture			
Scrubbing bathroom porcelain			
Organizing drawers, cupboards			
CLOTHES			
Ironing			
Doing laundry			
Mending, storing			
Wardrobe planning, shopping			
OUTSIDE TASKS			
Gardening			
Doing yard work			
Running errands			
Maintaining automobile			
Organizing, cleaning garage			
ADMINISTRATION			
Scheduling appointments			
Maintaining correspondence			
Maintaining records, paying bills			
MEMORIES			
Updating family photo albums			
Planning special days, creating traditions			

Meals

Person responsible for the grocery shopping:

Who will help?

Date and time to plan menus (use copy of form below) and make shopping list:

Date and time to go grocery shopping:

Grocery budget (weekly): _____   Grocery budget (monthly): _____

MENU PLANNER   FOR WEEK OF _____

	Breakfast	Lunch	Dinner
SUN.			
MON.			
TUES.			
WED.			
THUR.			
FRI.			
SAT.			

Housecleaning

Person responsible for…

- picking up clutter:

- dusting, polishing furniture:

- washing windows:

- vacuuming, cleaning floors:

- organizing drawers, cupboards:

- scrubbing bathroom porcelain:

Person responsible for giving attention to fix-it list and making sure things function:

Budget for household maintenance:

Household wish list:

Redecorate, paint, wallpaper (colors, patterns, styles)

Furniture

Miscellaneous items

Clothes

Laundry baskets are located: (Should they be more accessible?)

Person responsible for laundry

- sort: • wash:

- hang, dry: • iron:

- fold: • put away:

- mend: • store:

- plan wardrobe, shop:

Clothes to purchase in the fall (list sizes and colors):

Clothes to purchase in the spring (list sizes and colors):

Clothing to be packed away for summer and taken out for winter:

Clothing to be packed away for winter and taken out for summer:

Outside Tasks

Who will be responsible for gardening and yard work?

Who will help with…

- watering:
- raking:
- fertilizing:

- weeding:
- mowing:

Additional tools needed:

Gardening and yardwork budget?

What date in early spring will you sit down and plan?

What weekends in the fall will you reserve for cleanup and maintenance?

Who will be responsible for auto maintenance?

Who will help

- washing:
- cleaning interior:

- vacuuming:

Who will keep track of mileage to schedule oil change, lube and tune up?

Who will check water, gas, and tire pressure?

Who will be responsible for maintaining organization of garage?

Who will help clean the garage? What dates will you establish for this?

Who will run the errands?

- bank
- cleaners
- video returns
- pharmacy

- post office
- library
- repairs
- other:

Administration

Indicate the person responsible for each of these, and the best time to do them…

- determining monthly budget
- tracking expenditures

- balancing the checkbook
- paying the bills

- organizing tax records and preparing tax return (for accountant)

- researching insurance needs and coverage and making claims

- taking care of family correspondence

Person responsible for scheduling appointments:

- dental checkups
- vaccinations

- haircuts
- pet care

When is the best time to review the bookkeeping together?

Organizing Household Tasks

PUT YOUR homemaking evaluation into chart form (see pages 104-105) in order to keep it easy to refer to and update regularly.

1. Make a list of the chores in your home necessary to keep your lives running smoothly.

2. Break each chore into specific steps.

3. ☞ Make notes on preparation needed beforehand.

4. Negotiate your way through the specified jobs, one by one, assigning each task to an individual for an initial term of one month.

Making Housework Fun

Here are some starters. Brainstorm for other ideas, too:

- Play music. Decide beforehand to take a break or stop working at the end of a certain song.

- Make a game of it! When sorting and matching socks, for instance, sit in a circle round a laundry basket full of socks and take turns dipping into the basket with closed eyes and pulling out one sock. Continue to do so, folding into matched pairs or skipping your turn by trading socks with another player. When the basket is empty, the one who has the most matched pairs of socks is the winner. (For every sock without a mate, deduct one point.)

- Blitz the house before supper. Set the timer for five minutes. Give everyone a basket, box, or grocery bag and see how full they can fill it with clutter before the timer rings. The one with the most clutter wins! Each participant then puts their items where they belong before the timer rings after another five minutes.

- Your own ideas for making housework fun…

- Ideas for older kids…

5. Designate an established weekly (or daily) time set aside for the chore.

6. Specify a reward when a job is completed and inspected.

After going through this process, one father commented:

"We appreciate each other more now. The children have learned how discouraging it feels to have clutter left in their assigned cleanup area, and that a tremendous amount of effort goes into planning and carrying through fun family activities.

"Although there are times when each of us think we are doing more than anybody else, we have found out it is important to share the work. I guess we're about even when all is said and done."

Household Task Organizational Chart

Chore	Steps to Complete	✔	Notes	Person Responsible for each step	Time	Reward for Completion	✔

Household Task Organizational Chart

Chore	Steps to Complete	✔	Notes	Person Responsible for each step	Time	Reward for Completion	✔

Making Memories

Use the boxes on this and the following pages to help you make the most of special days and holidays in your family. Choose occasions from the list below, as well as other special days your family chooses to observe.

HOLIDAYS: New Year's Day, Valentine's Day, Passover, Easter Sunday, Mother's Day, Memorial Day, Father's Day, Independence Day, Labor Day, Halloween, Thanksgiving, Hanukkah, Christmas, New Year's Eve.

OTHER SPECIAL DAYS: all your birthdays; wedding anniversay; first and last days of school; national holidays of your cultural origins; a distinguished ancestor's birthday; days of personal milestones and accomplishment — losing a first tooth, getting straight A's, completing a project, winning the big game; first snowfall; first buds in spring; and many more...

Under "TRADITIONS":
- What is the significance of this day to your family?
  - What family traditions will you carry out?

Under "THIS YEAR'S CELEBRATION":
- Who will we celebrate with, and where?
  - Food and decoration plans:
    - Gifts involved:
    - What will you wear?
  - Budget for the celebration:
- Person responsible for planning:

TRADITIONS:

THIS YEAR'S CELEBRATION:

_____
(holiday or special day)

TRADITIONS:

THIS YEAR'S CELEBRATION:

_____
(holiday or special day)

TRADITIONS:	THIS YEAR'S CELEBRATION:
_____ (holiday or special day)	

TRADITIONS:	THIS YEAR'S CELEBRATION:
_____ (holiday or special day)	

TRADITIONS:	THIS YEAR'S CELEBRATION:
_____ (holiday or special day)	

TRADITIONS:	THIS YEAR'S CELEBRATION:
_____ (holiday or special day)	

Under "TRADITIONS":

- What is the significance of this day to your family?
- What family traditions will you carry out?

Under "THIS YEAR'S CELEBRATION":

- Who will we celebrate with, and where?
  - Food and decoration plans:
    - Gifts involved:
    - What will you wear?
  - Budget for the celebration:
- Person responsible for planning:

TRADITIONS:	THIS YEAR'S CELEBRATION:
_____ (holiday or special day)	

TRADITIONS:	THIS YEAR'S CELEBRATION:
_____ (holiday or special day)	

TRADITIONS:	THIS YEAR'S CELEBRATION:
_____ (holiday or special day)	

TRADITIONS:	THIS YEAR'S CELEBRATION:
_____ (holiday or special day)	

Under "TRADITIONS":

- What is the significance of this day to your family?
- What family traditions will you carry out?

Under "THIS YEAR'S CELEBRATION":

- Who will we celebrate with, and where?
  - Food and decoration plans:
    - Gifts involved:
    - What will you wear?
  - Budget for the celebration:
- Person responsible for planning:

TRADITIONS:	THIS YEAR'S CELEBRATION:
(holiday or special day)	

TRADITIONS:	THIS YEAR'S CELEBRATION:
(holiday or special day)	

TRADITIONS:	THIS YEAR'S CELEBRATION:
(holiday or special day)	

TRADITIONS:	THIS YEAR'S CELEBRATION:
(holiday or special day)	

Under "TRADITIONS":
- What is the significance of this day to your family?
- What family traditions will you carry out?

Under "THIS YEAR'S CELEBRATION":
- Who will we celebrate with, and where?
- Food and decoration plans:
- Gifts involved:
- What will you wear?
- Budget for the celebration:
- Person responsible for planning:

TRADITIONS:	THIS YEAR'S CELEBRATION:

_____
(holiday or special day)

TRADITIONS:	THIS YEAR'S CELEBRATION:

_____
(holiday or special day)

TRADITIONS:	THIS YEAR'S CELEBRATION:

_____
(holiday or special day)

TRADITIONS:	THIS YEAR'S CELEBRATION:

_____
(holiday or special day)

Under "TRADITIONS":
- What is the significance of this day to your family?
- What family traditions will you carry out?

Under "THIS YEAR'S CELEBRATION":
- Who will we celebrate with, and where?
- Food and decoration plans:
- Gifts involved:
- What will you wear?
- Budget for the celebration:
- Person responsible for planning:

Holiday Memories

The first holiday may have been invented to celebrate fertility or planting or harvest, but we're sure a mother was behind it. Even then she must have known that nothing could cure her day-to-day drudgery as well as a holiday or brighten the eye of a small child so quickly....

Whether you encourage these holidays or not, we don't think a month should go by without a celebration of some sort, even if you have to invent it. However, the only thing worse than having a month without a holiday is having a holiday without your child's help. He has every right to be a part of the preparation of each festivity, as he is a part of everything else that happens in a family.

When he polishes the silver bowl, roasts pecans or draws the place cards, he'll anticipate the party that much more — and that's where most of the fun comes from. The celebration itself will be over in hours, but the memory of those giddy days of preparation will last for years.

MARGUERITE KELLY and ELIA PARSONS, *The Mother's Almanac*

Your Vacation

Person responsible for planning the next family vacation?

Possible destinations:

Things to see and do there:

Tentative dates: Vacation budget:

Reservations required?   Date for making reservations:

Transportation: Estimated travel time:

Contents of automobile activity kit:

Other reminders…

Another important family task in making memories:
Select someone to be responsible to keep photo albums up to date.

Coordinating Family Time

Hold fast the time. Guard it, watch over it,
every hour, every minute. Unguarded it slips away,
like a lizard, smooth, slippery, faithless.
Hold every minute sacred.

THOMAS MANN

OUR HOME IS NESTLED in the Oregon woods, surrounded by pine trees and high desert sage. Outside its walls, all is peace and serenity. Inside, there is often clamor and noise and persistent efforts to make the wheels go around so that all five cogs mesh and whir steadily and smoothly.

But of all the efforts our family puts into it, none is greater than the effort to *get rid* of clutter and *find* time. *Fewer* dog-eared tennis shoes, fewer dolls and a lot fewer pieces of paper floating around; *more* golden hours and moments is what our family needs.

I heard Whitney Houston sing, "Give me one moment in time…one brief shining moment." Her plaintive prayer stirred me deeply even though what the writer of that song had in mind was, most likely, a far cry from what I envision at the mention of *one brief shining moment.*

If that moment *were* to come to me, how would I use it? And what would I do to make it shine? Initially, that doesn't seem problematic. I have a project list two miles long. Barely do I get started on one project before I get three new ideas. And I carry around at least three tons of dreams everywhere I go.

Those dreams continually feed my mental energy. My physical energy, however, is no match.

Good thing, too. Otherwise, I'd be plunging ahead into urgencies I have no business being involved in — urgencies that might desensitize me to the important issues…

…like shy pinks and brilliant golds on the Cascade horizon at sundown

…the slinking rise of early morning

light over the form of a man whose gentleness makes him strong.

...the vibrant patterns of a five-year-old's imagination: "When I grow up I want to be a babysitter, a singer, and a pirate!"

The important issues don't come crashing into my schedule the way telephone calls and drop-in visitors do. They never quite get their rightful place unless I stop and linger and wait. But in my seeming one-hundred-mile-a-minute lifestyle with husband and household, kids and career, one moment in time seems too much to ask, utterly beyond my reach.

I'm reaching for it, anyway, and when I find it — somewhere underneath the dirty socks and junk mail — I'm gonna make it shine by investing it in the important things. The struggle may be constant and exhausting, bringing moments of discouragement and despair — but sticking it out is worth it.

Time with my family has no substitute.

couple time

Getting a Grip on Time

HIS: HERS:

What time of day do you consider your personal prime time?

In what areas of your life would you like to save time?

In what areas would you like to spend more time?

How much time weekly are you currently spending with your spouse?

How much of this is spent ironing out practical details?

113

HIS: HERS:

How much of our time together is spent concentrating on each other's needs and feelings?

When is your prime time for being together?

How much time weekly are you currently spending with your children?

How much of this is spent doing errands, chores, and other practical necessities?

How much time weekly do you spend alone with each child?

How much is spent concentrating on their needs and feelings?

When is the best time to be with each of your children?

What is your greatest personal weakness in managing your time?

What things would you like to be able to say no to?

What things would you like to be able to say yes to?

The Way I Spend My Time

Write the answers to the following questions in your notebooks as they are read aloud. Then discuss your answers with your parents.

- What do you wish you had more time for?
- What is your favorite way to use your time?
- What is your best time of day?
- How much time do you spend daily playing or doing just what you want to?
- How much time do you spend daily in school or structured activities?
- How much time do you spend daily on homework?
- How much time do you spend daily watching TV or videos?
- How much time do you spend with your mom and dad?
- How much time do you spend all by yourself?

TIME WITH MOM AND DAD

- When is the last time you had a good talk with your mom and dad?
- How do you feel when they take time to be with you?

  ☐ like a business appointment   ☐ like a fun date   ☐ like a chore that has to be done   ☐ like I'm a Very Important Person

- What would you like to spend time doing with your mom and dad?
- How do your parents usually respond when you ask them to do something together with you?

  ☐ "I'm too tired"   ☐ "Sure, let's do it right now"   ☐ "We don't have enough money"
  ☐ "Good idea, let's get the stuff we need"   ☐ "Keep quiet"   ☐ "Why didn't I think of that?"   ☐ Other responses:

- What is your favorite way to spend your time with your parents?
- When do you most enjoy being with them?

Time Wasters vs. Time for Each Other

Which of these are time wasters for you?

☐ Misplaced items   ☐ Junk mail   ☐ Drop-in visitors   ☐ Waiting for people
☐ Television   ☐ Lack of goals   ☐ Errands   ☐ Commuting time   ☐ Lack of preparation   ☐ Bad attitudes   ☐ Poor organization   ☐ Procrastination

(adapted from *Tools for Time Management*, by EDWARD R. DAYTON)

What can be done to minimize the time wasters in your life?

- What are your working/school hours? How many hours of the day are you in separate activities and places? How many hours of the day are you all together at home?

- Which parent is most available to handle snags or emergencies during the day? Which parent is most available to handle the children who wake up at night?

- How much time weekly do you spend together as a family?

- How do you usually spend that time?

- Do you feel it draws you closer to each other?

- Do you feel your time together as a family is…

    ☐ boring?   ☐ fun?   ☐ creative?   ☐ frustrating?
    ☐ uncomfortable?   ☐ misused?

- How much time do you feel is reasonable to spend together weekly?

- What do each of you like best to do together?

- What do you like least?

- In what ways can you create pockets of time for each other daily? Weekly? Monthly?

- What do you see as your greatest family weakness in time management?

- Who does this involve?

- What could you do to improve?

- What shortcuts could you take to work smarter, not harder?

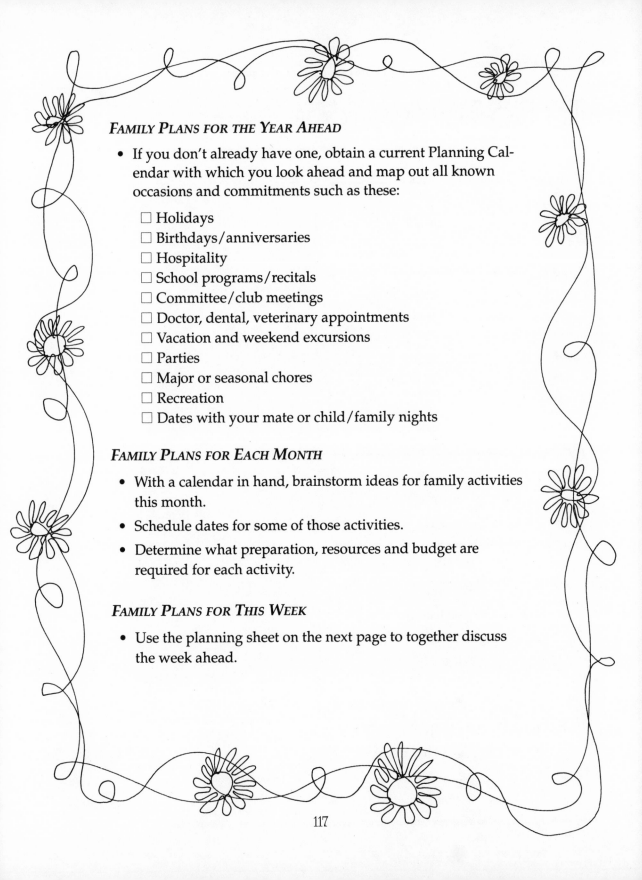

FAMILY PLANS FOR THE YEAR AHEAD

- If you don't already have one, obtain a current Planning Calendar with which you look ahead and map out all known occasions and commitments such as these:

  - ☐ Holidays
  - ☐ Birthdays/anniversaries
  - ☐ Hospitality
  - ☐ School programs/recitals
  - ☐ Committee/club meetings
  - ☐ Doctor, dental, veterinary appointments
  - ☐ Vacation and weekend excursions
  - ☐ Parties
  - ☐ Major or seasonal chores
  - ☐ Recreation
  - ☐ Dates with your mate or child/family nights

FAMILY PLANS FOR EACH MONTH

- With a calendar in hand, brainstorm ideas for family activities this month.

- Schedule dates for some of those activities.

- Determine what preparation, resources and budget are required for each activity.

FAMILY PLANS FOR THIS WEEK

- Use the planning sheet on the next page to together discuss the week ahead.

TO DO THIS WEEK OF _____

Monday
Family:

Personal:

Business:

Tuesday
Family:

Personal:

Business:

Wednesday
Family:

Personal:

Business:

Thursday
Family:

Personal:

Business:

Friday
Family:

Personal:

Business:

Saturday
Family:

Personal:

Business:

Sunday
Family:

Personal:

Business:

TO CALL:

TO WRITE:

TO BUY:

IF TIME PERMITS:

Becoming More Than We'd Imagined

Believing in Dreams

THE INSENSIBLE WATERS

We teach our children one thing only, as we were taught: to wake up. We teach our children to look alive there, to join by words and activities the life of human culture on the planet's crust. As adults we are almost all adept at waking up. We have so mastered the transition we have forgotten we ever learned it. Yet it is a transition we make a hundred times a day, as, like so many will-less dolphins, we plunge and surface, lapse and emerge. We live half our waking lives and all of our sleeping lives in some private, useless, and insensible waters we never mention or recall. Useless, I say. Valueless, I might add — until someone hauls their wealth up to the surface and into the wide-awake city, in a form that people can use.

ANNIE DILLARD, *Teaching a Stone to Talk*

AS I WAS GROWING UP, whenever we faced doubtful or uncertain circumstances, I heard my father quote Christopher Columbus. Had I learned no other lesson in life, I would have learned to "Sail on, sail on, sail on and on!" So often, this brought a serendipitous discovery to me. During my tender years of childhood and adolescence, Dad held out a guiding light of persistence, determination and faith. He showed me how to follow my dreams and build upon them.

A skilled parent is one who communicates a concise, imaginative vision while allowing it to be enhanced and clarified by children as they grow. Skilled parents bring awareness of personal possibilities to the surface of the family's conciousness. Children buy into their parents' vision when they experience the family as an energizing place where their gifts are appreciated and groomed. A sense of excitement and pride will result, and dreams will be conceived.

Do you encourage the dreams being formed in the shadowed corners of your child's soul? Becoming acquainted with them takes an intentional resolve to listen and watch. What kinds of play give your child the most joy? Which seem to occupy his imagination 100 percent? What makes your child's eyes light up?

The French Catholic priest Louis Evely, who has written eloquently of love and parenting in his book *Lovers in Marriage*, made it clear: "When you think you know someone, you no longer love him. When a parent passes final judgment on his child, when he claims to know what his child is 'really like,' when he fails to leave room for the infinite potential within his child, then he does not love his child any longer.... Love is not a blindfold, it is an eye-opener.... There is another kind of clarity that only comes with love: imagining what a person is capable of becoming. You begin to love each other when you begin to make something of each other."

A clear, bright, growing family vision is no accident. It is something we must ignite and inflame. A man with a brightened vision for his wife might say, "I want you to travel, do research on your project. It will inspire you. I'll stay home and take care of the kids." A mom who is in tune with the dreams of her son might say, "Go for it! Commit yourself to the training and see where it leads you. I'll cover the initial costs."

It is our happy privilege to participate in the hopes and aspirations of one another.

Personal Family Assessment:

Developing a warm, encouraging atmosphere and taking steps to kindle personal dreams doesn't happen all at once. The following exercises will begin to bring this issue to your family's awareness.

121

Facing Up to the Real Issues

HIS: HERS:

What are your personal dreams?

What ideas keep you awake at night?

In what areas are you gifted or talented?

What do you like to do most in your time off?

What are your dreams for your spouse?

In what areas is your spouse gifted or talented?

Complete these questions together:

- What are your dreams for each of your children?
- In what areas are each of your children gifted or talented?
- What kinds of play give your child the most joy? What kinds of things does he/she most often get excited about?

- What kind of training or education would help you develop your gifts? What about the gifts of your family members?
- About how much would the training cost?
- How soon could you reasonably begin?

- What supplies or equipment would facilitate development of each of your areas of talent?
- About how much would these cost?
- How soon would it be reasonable to purchase them? What upcoming occasions might be appropriate to give them as gifts to each other?

- What organizations or clubs could each of you join for support and inspiration in your individual areas of talent? (Look up phone numbers and addresses in the yellow pages for future reference.)
- Who would be a good resource person for each of your areas of talent or interest?

DO WE REALLY BELIEVE...

that no one wants to fail?

that people do what makes sense to THEM?

that people who seem lazy really aren't; they simply haven't been properly motivated?

that everyone wants to grow personally.

that everyone wants to make an important difference.

- Are we truly building a *family* — or am I fashioning personal dreams, and *using* the family to do it?
- In what ways are we communicating to our children that we want them to reach their fullest personal potential?

(adapted from *Leadership Confidence* by Bobb Biehl)

Fragile: Wishes Enclosed!

- The best thing I have ever experienced is…

☞ I want to get better at…

☞ I would like my family's help in this by…

☞ When I grow up I want to…

☞ When I grow up I want to be the kind of person who…

☞ If I knew for sure that I would not fail, I would…

☞ I think that I have special abilities in the area of…

- The best thing I have ever experienced is…

☞ I want to get better at…

☞ I would like my family's help in this by…

☞ When I grow up I want to…

☞ When I grow up I want to be the kind of person who…

☞ If I knew for sure that I would not fail, I would…

☞ I think that I have special abilities in the area of…

- The best thing I have ever experienced is…

☞ I want to get better at…

☞ I would like my family's help in this by…

☞ When I grow up I want to…

☞ When I grow up I want to be the kind of person who…

☞ If I knew for sure that I would not fail, I would…

☞ I think that I have special abilities in the area of…

Our Family Dream Journal

☞ Identify the dreams or ambitions of each member of your family. (As these are fulfilled, record here the date and how each dream was fulfilled.)

☞ Do you have a family dream — one that would involve all members of your family? If so, what is it?

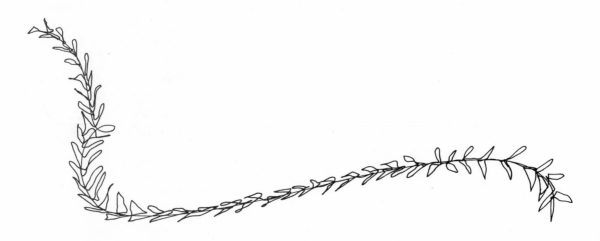

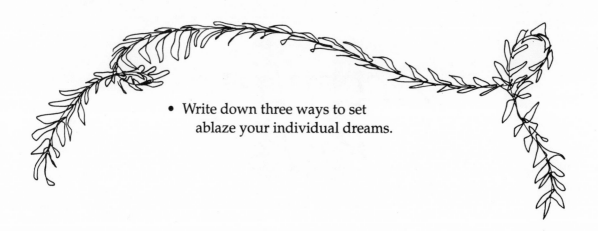

- Write down three ways to set
  ablaze your individual dreams.

- Write down three ways to set ablaze your family dream.

- Cut out pictures from magazines illustrating your family dream. It doesn't have to be something. The pictures might show people working together, exhibiting certain personality characteristics, or doing something unique together. Pictures will help your family dream become visual, and motivational speakers tell us visualization is the first step to making dreams come true. Post the pictures in a prominent place.

Accepting Risks

COURAGE TO BE TRANSPARENT

When the encounter and relationship of true love are missing in a human life, it is usually because the person has either selfishly or timidly kept the doors of his heart locked and barricaded. He is either unable or unwilling to risk transparency, to expose the most sensitive areas of his soul to another. Without such willingness to risk, human life can be only a prolonged pain of starvation and the whole world only a bleak prison. Answering the call to love demands much courage and determination because self-exposure always involves a risk of being seriously hurt. But without transparency love is impossible, and without love, human life is seriously incomplete.

JOHN POWELL, *The Secret of Staying in Love*

THE FAIRY TALE WRITER Hans Christian Andersen, often used the theme of vulnerability and courage. In his tale *The Wild Swans*, in which eleven brothers were cursed to fly as wild swans, Andersen developed this theme through the life of the brothers' younger sister Elisa. This innocent and pure-hearted princess willingly endured physical pain and emotional torment to redeem her brothers from the curse. Misunderstood and rejected by the prince who had loved her, Elisa persisted in her task of picking, crushing and knitting wild nettles into coats as her brothers' only antidote. She was eventually condemned as a witch for it, only to be rescued from death at the last possible second. Yet both tales present the two ingredients that I have also come to believe are absolutely essential to real love.

But opportunities to develop vulnerability and courage do not occur only in fairy tales. They are presented again and again in our own lives. And nowhere can they be developed more effectively than in family life. Rick Linamen believes that where parents have developed a plat-

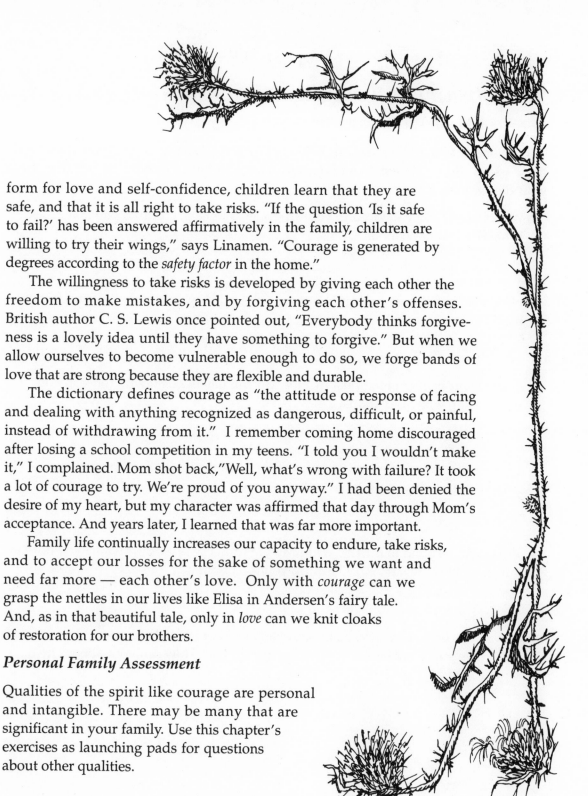

form for love and self-confidence, children learn that they are safe, and that it is all right to take risks. "If the question 'Is it safe to fail?' has been answered affirmatively in the family, children are willing to try their wings," says Linamen. "Courage is generated by degrees according to the *safety factor* in the home."

The willingness to take risks is developed by giving each other the freedom to make mistakes, and by forgiving each other's offenses. British author C. S. Lewis once pointed out, "Everybody thinks forgiveness is a lovely idea until they have something to forgive." But when we allow ourselves to become vulnerable enough to do so, we forge bands of love that are strong because they are flexible and durable.

The dictionary defines courage as "the attitude or response of facing and dealing with anything recognized as dangerous, difficult, or painful, instead of withdrawing from it." I remember coming home discouraged after losing a school competition in my teens. "I told you I wouldn't make it," I complained. Mom shot back,"Well, what's wrong with failure? It took a lot of courage to try. We're proud of you anyway." I had been denied the desire of my heart, but my character was affirmed that day through Mom's acceptance. And years later, I learned that was far more important.

Family life continually increases our capacity to endure, take risks, and to accept our losses for the sake of something we want and need far more — each other's love. Only with *courage* can we grasp the nettles in our lives like Elisa in Andersen's fairy tale. And, as in that beautiful tale, only in *love* can we knit cloaks of restoration for our brothers.

Personal Family Assessment

Qualities of the spirit like courage are personal and intangible. There may be many that are significant in your family. Use this chapter's exercises as launching pads for questions about other qualities.

Establishing a Foundation of Courage

—IN YOUR MARRIAGE RELATIONSHIP

Choose one or two of the questions below and write a letter to your spouse addressing those issues. Exchange letters and discuss what you have written. Record notes from your discussion here.

- What issues have you faced in your marriage that have required you take risks? What risks? What happened?

- How did your spouse respond last time you said, "I was wrong. Will you forgive me?"

- Hurts occur in every relationship. How do you usually deal with those in your relationship with your spouse?

- When you treat hurts as misunderstandings and deal with them by gentle confrontation or forgiveness, what is the outcome? How do you feel about it?

- When you respond to hurt by withdrawing from the person who hurt you or retaliating, what is the outcome? How do you feel about it?

☞ Have there been hurts caused in your childhood or youth that haven't been healed yet? Have you ever shared these with your spouse? How can your spouse help you deal with them?

—IN YOUR RELATIONSHIP WITH YOUR CHILDREN

- When your kids hurt or offend each other, what are your guidelines to facilitate character growth and healing?

- What do you believe *your* response should be when one of your children fails in a task or project, or in a relationship?

- What usually happens within the *family* when someone in your family fails?

- On a scale from 1 to 10, estimate the *safety factor* in your family.

☐	☐	☐	☐	☐	☐	☐	☐	☐	☐
1	2	3	4	5	6	7	8	9	10

10 = *perfect, healthy freedom to take on new challenges*
1 = *children fully expect to be harshly criticized for any failure*

- What happened the last time you said to your child, "Even though you made a mistake, you are completely forgiven"?

- What are you teaching your kids about loss? How are you teaching them?

Everybody Needs Courage

Complete these sentences in your notebooks. Then share your answers with each other.

- The last time I let my feelings show… (what happened?)
- The last time somebody made me look weak and foolish, I…
- I am willing to take risks in order to do something important to me because…
  - ☐ I love the thrill of facing the unknown.
  - ☐ It's worth it when I have the chance to achieve and win.
  - ☐ I know my family will support me even if I fail.
  - ☐ My family's love makes me feel confident.
  - ☐ other reasons:
- If I made a decision that later seemed like a mistake, I would feel…
- I think strength means being…
- I think weakness means…

Taking Risks

☞ What risks will you encounter as you make family decisions and face changes this year? List the specific details.

☐ risks inherent in residence or career changes?

☐ risks inherent in family structure changes?

☐ risks inherent in financial changes?

☐ other risks:

• What are the pros of making a specific major change?

• What are the cons?

☞ How might you minimize the risks that seem threatening?

1. By getting advice from friends or professionals

2. By talking about it with each other

3. By reading a book on the subject

4. By making schedule changes

5. Other ways:

☞ How can you develop courage to take risks as a family?

Thinking Creatively

DAUGHTER: Dad, can you write your name in the dark?
DAD: I think so.
DAUGHTER: Great. Would you please turn off the lights and sign my report card?

* * *

Letter from boarding school:

Dear Mom and Dad:
Gue$$ what I need? Plea$e $end $ome $oon.

Be$t Wi$he$,
Your $on $ammy

Letter from home:

Dear Sammy:
NOthing much is happening here. Please write aNOther letter soon.
Bye for NOw.

Love,
Dad and Mom

JOANNA COLE and STEPHANIE CALMENSON, *The Laugh Book*

I ALWAYS ASSUMED that raising kids meant bringing up children. But as my children grow I'm discovering that, as Phyllis Theroux phrased it, raising kids *really* means "lowering parents." I am forced down on eye level with my kids every day. And there I receive the best education available. My three girls, with their smudged chins and lively imaginations, are teaching me that meeting life with a childlike spirit is vital. Small children don't survey life with skepticism. Their magic eyes enable them to see miracles buried in hard, crusty shells.

Someone once said that "the angels speak to those who take time to walk with children." I found this out one afternoon while attempting to prepare a five-year-old friend to return home to rooms packed up in boxes. Her family was breaking up; I knew she had been through a difficult time. I was giving her my best little speech of consolation, when she looked at me with the world's brightest smile and said, "Yes, but the good thing is my chicken pox don't scratch anymore!"

Certainly she was unable to comprehend the tragedy about to crash down upon her, but I wondered as I drove her home: *Who came closer to transforming the heartache — she or I?* Her simplicity and innocence were stepping stones through the trauma. My definitive adult vantage point was lacking in perspective and power to help her. She helped *me*.

Authors Patricia Ward and Martha Stout have noted that "studies of unusually creative adults have shown that they...retain something of the child about them."

One artist who has proven this is children's author and illustrator Maurice Sendak. "Somewhere along the line in my work," he says, "I gained the insight that there is a subtle, complicated interrelationship between childhood and adulthood. To move from one to the other, you don't change the way a caterpillar does to become a butterfly. And you don't have to let go of one and quickly find the other before you can get over to the other side. In moving across, nothing is lost; in fact, you add to what you are."

This is the essence of thinking creatively. Innovative people discover new ways of dealing with the old and familiar through *play*, a process combining judgment and intuition. Whether it be solving problems, overcoming stumbling blocks or doing something never done before, the creative process requires the willingness to live with uncertainties for a period of time, to overlook complexities, and to dislodge ready-made answers.

Albert Einstein once asked, "Why do my best ideas come while I'm shaving?" I know two prolific writers who keep waterproof pens in the bathroom; each claims that his most productive ideas come to him in the shower. In the family, the moments you spend off guard with each other are the most precious moments you have. They will prepare you to receive the rough, undefined solutions and discoveries that can tumble your way when you open yourself to the playful mind.

We can never go back to being three feet tall, but we can get back in touch with the childlike spirit within. The best way to do this is to keep very close to the little ones in our own backyard.

Personal Family Assessment

This chapter was designed for practice in putting the playful mind to work, and to get you started thinking in creative ways about snags in your family life. These were not designed to end to all your problems, but to help you realize that problem solving can be fun, should be fun, and that most problems *will* be solved by keeping the process simple. The key here is: don't take yourselves too seriously. Accept the abstracts in your life. Concrete solutions are often arrived at by playing with unknown factors.

What Can We Learn From the Playful Mind?

☞ After identifying priority concerns in your marriage through the exercises below, proceed to the problem-solving steps on page 138. (Be patient. Solutions often require a period of incubation before they emerge.)

HERS:

In what areas are you most creative?

During what kinds of activities and situations do you get your best ideas?

Where do you hunt for ideas?

Can those creative abilities be used to tap into other areas where you feel uninspired? How?

Define one or two problem areas in your marriage that seem to have no solution:

On a scale of 1 to 10 indicate the importance to you of solving each of these problem areas (10= extremely important).

| PROBLEM: | _____ | SIGNIFICANCE: | 1 2 3 4 5 6 7 8 9 10 |
| PROBLEM: | _____ | SIGNIFICANCE: | 1 2 3 4 5 6 7 8 9 10 |

HIS:

In what areas are you most creative?

During what kinds of activities and situations do you get your best ideas?

Where do you hunt for ideas?

Can those creative abilities be used to tap into other areas where you feel uninspired? How?

Define one or two problem areas in your marriage that seem to have no solution:

On a scale of 1 to 10 indicate the importance to you of solving each of these problem areas (10= extremely important).

| PROBLEM: | _____ | SIGNIFICANCE: | 1 2 3 4 5 6 7 8 9 10 |
| PROBLEM: | _____ | SIGNIFICANCE: | 1 2 3 4 5 6 7 8 9 10 |

Tips to Greater Creativity

Parents, ask your kids one or two of these questions, and
really listen...

- Where do you get your best ideas? When do you get
  your best ideas?

- What happens when you play detective and ask what-if
  questions?

- If you could go somewhere far away or be someone silly, where would
  you go or who would you be? Why? What would you want to accomplish?

- What areas of life do you feel most enthusiastic about? Imagine yourself
  doing something in that area one year from now. What will you have
  accomplished?

THE CHALK DOT

When I was a sophomore in high school, my English teacher put a small chalk dot on the blackboard. He asked the class what it was. A few seconds passed and then someone said, "A chalk dot on the blackboard." The rest of the class seemed relieved that the obvious had been stated, and no one else had anything more to say.

"I'm surprised at you," the teacher told the class. "I did the same exercise yesterday with a group of kindergartners and they thought of fifty different things the chalk mark could be: an owl's eye, a cigar butt, the top of a tele-phone pole, a star, a pebble, a squashed bug, a rotten egg, and so on. They really had their imaginations in high gear."

In the ten year period between kindergarten and high school, not only had we learned how to find the right answer, we had also lost the ability to look for more than one right answer. We had learned how to be specific, but we had lost much of our imaginative power. As noted educator Neil Postman has remarked, "Children enter school as question marks and leave as periods."

ROGER VON OECH,
A Whack On The Side Of The Head

137

What Are We Going To Do About It?
(Ten Steps to Creative Problem Solving)

1 Identify two or three stumbling blocks that repeatedly come to the surface in your family.

2 Define one of these and state it from three different angles. (Try using the viewpoints of the people involved.)

3 In what ways would your family benefit by overcoming this stumbling block?

4 What might happen if you make an attempt to overcome it, but fail?

5 If the best possible outcome were to happen, what would it be?

6 Brainstorm alternative ways to overcome the problem. List as many as possible. Start with the obvious, but don't stay with safe ideas. Open the discussion to divergent directions.

7 Now drop your conversation and play a game or do something the whole family enjoys for a limited period of time.

8 Sit down again and identify the one solution that appears most workable for your family.

9 Write down your goal, or what you wish to accomplish by overcoming this stumbling block.

10 State four action steps that will help you get close to your goal.

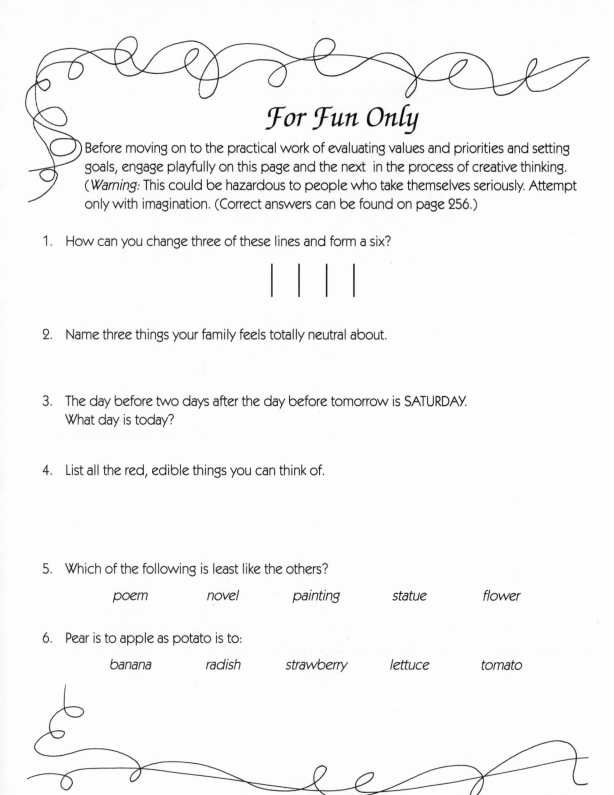

For Fun Only

Before moving on to the practical work of evaluating values and priorities and setting goals, engage playfully on this page and the next in the process of creative thinking. (*Warning:* This could be hazardous to people who take themselves seriously. Attempt only with imagination. (Correct answers can be found on page 256.)

1. How can you change three of these lines and form a six?

   | | | |

2. Name three things your family feels totally neutral about.

3. The day before two days after the day before tomorrow is SATURDAY. What day is today?

4. List all the red, edible things you can think of.

5. Which of the following is least like the others?

   poem   *novel*   *painting*   *statue*   *flower*

6. Pear is to apple as potato is to:

   banana   *radish*   *strawberry*   *lettuce*   *tomato*

7. Play these two button puzzles:

First, move *only three* of these buttons to make the triangle turn upside down.

Second, move *only one* of these buttons and make two rows that are each three pennies long.

8. If it were two hours later, it would be half as long until midnight as it would be if it were an hour later. What time is it now?

9. Continue the following number series below with the two numbers which continue the series.

1   10   3   9   5   8   7   7   9   6   ?   ?

10. In the following line of letters, cross out ten letters so that the remaining six letters, without altering their sequence, will spell a familiar English word.

BSAINXLEATNTEARS

Renewing Our Purpose & Vision

Clarifying Family Values

SIX TRUTHS FOR TEACHING YOUR CHILD VALUES

1. Children ultimately make their own choices.... Don't measure your parenting performance solely by how well your child complies with each of your preferences.

2. If you think you've largely failed so far, it is never too late to start doing what's right.

3. Modeling is the bottom line. Example is a difficult taskmaster, but no teacher is more effective.

4. No parent is an island. Watch for situations, create opportunities where your child is exposed to other adults you admire.

5. Your child's sense of security is not rooted as much in your love for the child as in how much love he or she knows you and your spouse share.

6. Kids forgive much easier and forget longer than parents do. It takes a lot of consistently negative experiences to sour your relationship with your child. So if he or she knows it is your deepest desire to be a fair and effective parent, your relationship can survive many mistakes without irreparable damage.

PAUL LEWIS, *40 Ways to Teach Your Child Values*

* * *

MANY OF US GREW UP with mental pictures of the Sunday dinner table spread with white linen and the extended family sitting around it, happily sharing the pot roast or fried chicken. As a child, I experienced such dinners on my grandparents' Kansas farm. But within a generation, such family norms have all but evaporated as a different family future became present reality.

Arnold H. Glasow wrote, "The trouble with the future is that it usually arrives before we're ready for it." Rapid changes within the last thirty years have created incredible time warps. When we try to plug yesterday's values into today's social and economic realities, peculiar distortions occur. We experience what Alvin Toffler called *future shock*.

Instead of setting impossible standards based on bygone days, it is important to clarify our values regularly. Attitudes and ideals are still changing. Sometimes an encounter with what we *think we believe*, but *no longer live by* is enough to shake us up and get us thinking.

I still believe in old-fashioned Sundays, so I structure my work week to keep that day free to relax. On the other hand, Sunday dinner is often just pizza served picnic style on our patio. Some values inherited from my midwestern '50s childhood have been discarded along with the deep fat fryer, while others I cherish and hope to pass on.

Values are eloquently expressed through the priorities we set. Priorities are clues to what really is important to us. Our *checkbook* registry reveals some of our secrets. Our *date book* is another tattletale. Values begin where we put our time, money and energy. Our children witness how we spend these practical quantities and internalize what they see. Are we replacing values of the human spirit with the values of a material world? Are we losing touch with feelings in our efforts not to lose out on things? What will be important when we look back years from now?

Chrysler's superstar executive Lee Iacocca had this to say: "As I start the twilight years of my life, I try to look back and figure out what it was all about. I'm still not sure what is meant by good fortune and success. I know fame and power are for the birds. But then life suddenly comes into focus. There stand my kids. And I love them."

What Are Our Values?

Of the categories of values listed below, which four are most important to you?
(Mark them with a check — ✔) Which four categories are least important to you?
(Mark those with an ✗)

HIS: HERS:

☐	☐	1. Prosperity
☐	☐	2. Accomplishment (a lasting contribution)
☐	☐	3. Benevolence (social justice, helping others)
☐	☐	4. Family harmony
☐	☐	5. Freedom (independence, free choice)
☐	☐	6. Moral integrity (freedom from inner conflicts)
☐	☐	7. Sexual and personal intimacy
☐	☐	8. Power (the ability to influence events and make things happen)
☐	☐	9. Spiritual development (salvation)
☐	☐	10. Friendship (companionship)
☐	☐	11. Wisdom and aesthetics (a contemplative way of life)
☐	☐	12. Recognition (fame)
☐	☐	13. Personal growth and creativity (self-development)
☐	☐	14. Excitement and adventure (a stimulating, active life)

(Adapted from GAIL SHEEHY, *Pathfinders*)

- Are there any other values you would add to your personal list of those highest in importance?

- Discuss together how your own lives reflect the values you believe are most important. Record your thoughts here:

- What do your checkbook and your date book tell you about these values?

- Tell *why* these values are important to each of you.

HIS: HERS:

☞ Write down three specific ways you would like one or more of these important values to take expression in the lives of your children.

An example:
I believe in the value of *freedom*. I want my daughter to…
- be able to make her own decisions
- earn an honest living in the career of her choice
- be emotionally independent of what others think of her or pressure her to do.

☞ Name two ways to teach this value to each of your children.

What Is Most Important to Me?

Kids, please score your answers to each question below like this:

Very True = 9   Sometimes True = 6   Not Sure = 3   Not True = 0

Again, record your answers under the column headed by your initials. After you've answered the question, you can turn the page to see the scoring procedure.

1. I would rather own a big fancy home than an expensive piece of art.
2. It is just as important to learn about art and music as math and history.
3. I enjoy making things with my hands.
4. If I can't be a club leader than I wouldn't want to be in the club.
5. People make the most interesting subjects for books.
6. I think it would be fun to be a TV performer.
7. I want to be a writer someday and I've already started to practice.
8. I want to make my parents proud of me whatever I do.
9. If I got lost in a forest the first thing I would do is pray.
10. If somebody tries to pressure me to do something that's not right, I get away.
11. I want to do something that will be recognized by a lot of other people.
12. I might like to climb a mountain someday.
13. I want to live in a house with a beautiful garden.
14. I like to give presents I've made myself.
15. If I believe something I won't let anybody talk me out of it — not even for money.
16. I think it would be fun to work in a big, foreign city.
17. I look forward to having my own kids someday.
18. I like to study about how mechanical things work.
19. I want to work for myself so I can decide when and how long I'll work.
20. I want a career that takes me out among people to do something for them.
21. I think it is important to go to church with my family.
22. I'd rather be a principal of a school than a teacher.
23. I wouldn't like to go camping in the woods where there are no other people.
24. No matter what I do in life, I want to spend a lot of time with my family.
25. Being on a TV game show based on chance would make me faint from nerves.
26. I would like to design and sew my own clothes.
27. Money isn't everything, but lack of money isn't anything.

☐ ☐ ☐ 28. I would like to become a star so I could be rich.

☐ ☐ ☐ 29. I would like to become a star so I could become famous.

☐ ☐ ☐ 30. I would like to become a star so I could travel all over the world.

☐ ☐ ☐ 31. Some of my friends don't believe in God, but I know He is real.

☐ ☐ ☐ 32. I'd rather be a doctor than a lawyer.

☐ ☐ ☐ 33. I'm smart and it would be fun to help kids who have trouble learning.

☐ ☐ ☐ 34. I like going back to the same places on vacations better than trying new places.

☐ ☐ ☐ 35. I have my own *Bible*, and I try to read it every day.

☐ ☐ ☐ 36. It's fun to stay home and play together with my brothers and sisters.

☐ ☐ ☐ 37. I want to earn a lot of money, even though I may not like the kind of work I do.

☐ ☐ ☐ 38. If I were a writer, I'd write a how-to-do-something book before I'd write a science fiction thriller.

☐ ☐ ☐ 39. I'd take off on a moment's notice if given the chance to fly to Paris or London.

☐ ☐ ☐ 40. I want to get married and spend my life with someone special.

☐ ☐ ☐ 41. If something is risky, I'll be the first to try it.

☐ ☐ ☐ 42. I love the changing of nature's seasons and the beauty in each one.

☐ ☐ ☐ 43. I love learning about things I've never heard of or seen before.

☐ ☐ ☐ 44. If the forests were about to be destroyed, I'd work to save them.

☐ ☐ ☐ 45. I'd like to stand on the highest stair as an Olympic winner or wear the crown of Miss America.

☐ ☐ ☐ 46. I love doing things and going places with my friends.

☐ ☐ ☐ 47. There is a right and a wrong, and problems result when you mix them up.

☐ ☐ ☐ 48. I like to bounce my ideas and problems off other members of my family and find out what they think about them.

☐ ☐ ☐ 49. I do my best when I work alone. Teamwork is not the way I work best.

☐ ☐ ☐ 50. The universe fascinates me, so does mother earth and the way nature works.

☐ ☐ ☐ 51. I prefer to be with people as much as possible.

☐ ☐ ☐ 52. I am at my best when I'm in charge of something.

☐ ☐ ☐ 53. I want to be in a career where I decide what I want to do — even if it means earning less money.

☐ ☐ ☐ 54. Nobody is going to talk me into taking risks with my money.

☐ ☐ ☐ 55. Traveling doesn't interest me — especially if it means not being able to maintain friendships.

☐ ☐ ☐ 56. I enjoy being asked for my opinion — I think I have good ideas.

Adapted from *Choices,* pp. 93-96, © Girls Club of Santa Barbara.
Used by permission of Advocacy Press, P.O. Box 236, Santa Barbara, CA 93102.

NOW ADD UP your scores from the previous pages, according to the way the question numbers are grouped on this page. By comparing your scores on each category, you'll have an objective indication of what values are most important to you right now. The higher the score in an area, the higher the value you place on it.

Question number:	your scores:		
(17)	____	____	____
(24)	____	____	____
(36)	____	____	____
(48)	____	____	____
TOTAL	____	____	____

FAMILY

Question number:	your scores:		
(12)	____	____	____
(16)	____	____	____
(30)	____	____	____
(41)	____	____	____
TOTAL	____	____	____

ADVENTURE

Question number:	your scores:		
(5)	____	____	____
(18)	____	____	____
(43)	____	____	____
(50)	____	____	____
TOTAL	____	____	____

KNOWLEDGE

Question number:	your scores:		
(4)	____	____	____
(22)	____	____	____
(52)	____	____	____
(56)	____	____	____
TOTAL	____	____	____

POWER

Question number:	your scores:		
(1)	____	____	____
(27)	____	____	____
(28)	____	____	____
(37)	____	____	____
TOTAL	____	____	____

MONEY

Question number:	your scores:		
(8)	____	____	____
(10)	____	____	____
(15)	____	____	____
(47)	____	____	____
TOTAL	____	____	____

MORAL JUDGMENT AND PERSONAL CONSISTENCY

Question number:	your scores:		
(40)	____	____	____
(46)	____	____	____
(51)	____	____	____
(55)	____	____	____
TOTAL	____	____	____

FRIENDSHIP & COMPANIONSHIP

Question number:	your scores:		
(6)	____	____	____
(11)	____	____	____
(29)	____	____	____
(45)	____	____	____
TOTAL	____	____	____

RECOGNITION

Question number:	your scores:		
(2)	____	____	____
(13)	____	____	____
(42)	____	____	____
(44)	____	____	____
TOTAL	____	____	____

LOVE OF BEAUTY

Question number:	your scores:		
(3)	____	____	____
(7)	____	____	____
(14)	____	____	____
(26)	____	____	____
TOTAL	____	____	____

CREATIVITY

Question number:	your scores:		
(20)	____	____	____
(19)	____	____	____
(33)	____	____	____
(38)	____	____	____
TOTAL	____	____	____

HELPING OTHERS

Question number:	your scores:		
(19)	____	____	____
(25)	____	____	____
(49)	____	____	____
(53)	____	____	____
TOTAL	____	____	____

INDEPENDENCE

Question number:	your scores:		
(25)	____	____	____
(34)	____	____	____
(23)	____	____	____
(54)	____	____	____
TOTAL	____	____	____

SECURITY

Question number:	your scores:		
(9)	____	____	____
(21)	____	____	____
(31)	____	____	____
(35)	____	____	____
TOTAL	____	____	____

SPIRITUAL DEVELOPMENT

About Values

- What primary values do you all hold in common?

- How do your individual values intertwine with each other? In what ways do they conflict with each other?

- In the spaces below, work together to write statements about:
    (1) How you as a family define each of those important values
    (2) Why these values are important to you.

Value: _____

Value: _____

Value: _____

Value: _____

Evaluating Family Priorities

RAISE THE SHINING BARRIER

We both love strawberries and ships and collies and poems and all beauty, and all those things bind us together. Those sharings just happened to be; but what we must do now is share everything. Everything! If one of us likes anything, there must be something to like in it — and the other one must find it. Every single thing that either of us likes. That way we shall create a thousand strands, great and small, that will link us together....

Through sharing we would not only make a bond of incredible friendship, but through sharing we would keep the magic of inloveness....

The failure of love might seem to be caused by hate or boredom or unfaithfulness with a lover; but those were results. First came the creeping separateness; the failure behind the failure.

We raised the shining Barrier against creeping separateness, which was, in the last analysis, self. We also raised it against a world of indecencies and decaying standards, the decline of courtesy, the whispering mockers of love.

SHELDON VANAUKEN, *A Severe Mercy*

THE PROCESS OF EVALUATING your priorities and establishing new ones if necessary, is based on the clarification of your values. The values esteemed by the couple in the excerpt quoted above were *friendship* and *inloveness*. This couple made a conscious decision to make *sharing everything* their top priority, and to keep high standards of decency, courtesy, and faithfulness.

In this chapter we want to determine how to use our limited time, energy, and money in a way that will enable us to stay true to our personal values. To do this, we must be ready for trade-offs.

To prioritize is to give a preferred rating to a commodity in limited supply. If, for example, *family fun and recreation* is one of the values your family has chosen, you will ask yourselves questions leading to practical decisions, such as: What sacrifices is our family willing to make so we can afford seasonal extras like weekend fishing excursions or a ski trip? How will we structure weekends so we give a high priority to recreational fun of all kinds?

If *integrity* and *faith* are important values to your family, you will ask questions that lead you to develop a lifestyle that serves those values. You might ask: Where will we educate our children: neighborhood school, private school, home school? What trade-offs will our decision require? What kind of friendships will we cultivate? What kind of books and toys will we have at home?

Your priorities should be a reflection of the principles you want to build your lives on. Although those principles may or may not change greatly over a lifetime, you will probably need to change priorities frequently according to the changing seasons or circumstances of your life.

Sometimes I become aware of a certain area I know should be given top priority, but working it out seems terribly inconvenient and out of reach — such as making pockets of time in crowded schedules for my children individually. Making this kind of priority becomes a complicated acrobatic maneuver requiring, in some cases, raw faith that other things will take care of themselves. I ask myself questions to clarify what is really important and what is merely urgent;

questions like, "What price will I pay ten or twenty years from now if I do not spend time today with the people I love?"

Keys to setting priorities:

• Define the important issues, based on your values, and address those first.

• Plan the predictable, and allow space for the unpredictable. (There will always be added demands!)

• Anticipate emotional and practical needs, and tackle them head-on. (Become an expert in reading the feelings behind the faces in your family.)

On the subject of values and priorities, one father wrote his daughter: *"Now I'm glad my parents insisted on the piano lessons. And here's the reason I'm insisting on yours, too. There will be days later in life when you feel lonely or depressed. There may be a lot of people around you and there may be many words spoken to you. But they will not bring you comfort. That will be the time to communicate with the masters, to speak the language of art in order to receive what cannot be bought, begged or borrowed.*

"You may never become a ballerina or a concert pianist. That's fine. But I want you to learn the basics in disciplining the way you express yourself, and I want you to learn a variety of expressions. Along the way you may receive new visions for your own life and enough inspiration to pass on to somebody else" (Ben Alex, *Magic Moments*).

Priorities for Busy People

Make a list of twenty things you have to do this month and put them in order of most importance. Then share your lists with each other. On the right is an example of one parent's personal priority list (!).

His:	Hers:	Superparent:
		1. Return proofs of new book to publisher
		2. Interview with Barbara Walters
		3. Conference with kids' teachers
		4. Testify before Senate committee
		5. Make school play costume for Muffy
		6. Cammie's Little League game
		7. Romantic evening with Robin
		8. Start research for new book
		9. Repair home computer
		10. Weed vegetable garden
		11. Take flying lesson
		12. Change oil in Mercedes
		13. Clean toilets
		14. Read newspaper
		15. Bake brownies
		16. Workout at the gym
		17. Paint mural on front hall wall
		18. Polish furniture
		19. Wax no-wax floor
		20. Sleep
		(Adapted from *Choices*)

FIVE TIPS FOR SETTING PRIORITIES:

Explore alternatives to your current use of time, money, energy.
Ease away from the urgent (by dealing with it before it becomes a problem).
Embrace the important by taking a hard look at your values.
Experiment with what works best for your family.
Endeavor to enjoy each other.

Evaluate each other's priority list on the opposite page, and check off any overlapping priorities.

- Which items on your lists can be done more effectively (for either practical or emotional reasons) by doing them together?

- Where can your priorities be traded or delegated?

☞ In occurrences of conflicting priorities,
    Whose are more important?
    Whose are most urgent?

☞ Which should be done first?

☞ *Learning to Focus*

- Kids, name one of the nicest things your Mom or Dad or one of your siblings ever did for you.

- Parents, name one of the nicest things your spouse or one of your children ever did for you.

- What are your favorite family celebrations? Why?

- What family traditions are important to you?

☞ What new family traditions would you like to initiate this year?

✍ What kinds of family activities do you love? List in your notebooks (and take notes here on the family's discussion of them).

✍ What kinds of family activities do you dislike? List four or five in your notebooks.

- What changes would you make if you had been told you had only one year to live?

- Compare with each other your lists of favorite family traditions and activities; then make a *common* list of the things *all* of you love to do.

☞ When would be the best possible times to do these activities together?

How often?

- What resources or materials do you need to do these activities together regularly?

- What things that you do not like to do are you willing to do in a trade for other family members doing what you like to do — though they may not enjoy those things?

- What *daily* family rituals are important to you?
  ☐ A good-bye hug   ☐ Saying grace at meals   ☐ Having a snack together after school   ☐ Shooting baskets after supper   ☐ Watching a favorite TV show together   ☐ Tucking or getting tucked into bed   ☐ Other rituals

- What energizes your family life when you are all home together?
  ☐ Tickling   ☐ Eating   ☐ Talking   ☐ Playing   ☐ Chores   ☐ Anything else?

- What seems to drain your sense of togetherness when you are all home together?
  ☐ Teasing   ☐ Bickering   ☐ Talking   ☐ TV   ☐ Chores   ☐ Anything else?

Friends & Relatives

- What friends and relatives do you correspond with? How often?

- How important is this to you? How important do you believe your correspondence is to each of these people?

- Is there anyone you want to drop from the list?

- Are there others you want to add?

- What friends and relatives do you regularly telephone? How often?

- How important is this to you? How important do you believe it is to these people?

- Is there anyone you want to drop from the list?

- Are there others you want to add?

- What friends and relatives do you celebrate holidays with?

- How important is this to you? How important do you believe it is to each of these people?

- Is there anyone you want to drop from the list?

- Are there others you want to add?

Catagorizing Family Priorities

What priorities can you identify as especially important for a healthy emotional environment in your home?

Which priorities primarily involve only the practical functioning of the home:

What do you think is the relationship between these to kinds of priorities?

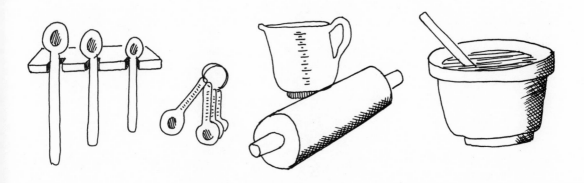

Project for Priorities

Look back again at the four most important values for your family which you identified and defined in the last chapter. Record now *priorities* that are important to living out each value you've identified.

Value # 1: _____

        Priorities:

Value # 1: _____

        Priorities:

Value # 1: _____

        Priorities:

Value # 1: _____

        Priorities:

Family Talks About Trade-offs

☞ You've now clarified your values and established priorities. In each of the three following ways, what tradeoffs will your family have to make in order to follow those priorities and live by your chosen values?

Time Tradeoffs —

    Value #1

    Value #2

    Value #3

    Value #4

Money Tradeoffs —

    Value #1

    Value #2

    Value #3

    Value #4

Energy Tradeoffs —

    Value #1

    Value #2

    Value #3

    Value #4

Formulating a Family Creed

STARS AS NO ONE ELSE HAS THEM

"All men have the stars," he answered, "but they are not the same things for different people. For some, who are travelers, the stars are guides. For others they are no more than little lights in the sky. For others, who are scholars, they are problems. For my businessman they were wealth. But all these stars are silent. You — you alone — will have the stars as no one else has them ...."

ANTOINE DE SAINT-EXUPERY, *The Little Prince*

MY HUSBAND AND I looked forward to the birth of our first child with idealism and determination. We set sail, expecting to raise a happy, cohesive family in a harmonious atmosphere like the one easily created with matching quilts and curtains in the nursery. But somewhere along the way, we realized that parents and children *become* families through interaction with each other down the years and over the changing seasons.

The waves that crash and the gales that blow lend credibility to our lives, give authority to our experience. We learned that to chart a course by the stars is not just to cast our gaze outward and sail away, hoping to drop anchor off a shining beach somewhere. It is to struggle with the elements, tangle with the storms

— and have a firm understanding of why we are doing it.

This understanding is what is meant by *family creed* — a statement of purpose defining the philosophical, ethical or theological reasons for making the journey. Measurable goals propel us forward, but we are not in competition with other families. We must allow *long-term perspectives* to determine the individual direction and speed for our family journey.

Draw your family creed from *your* unique perspective. Define what you believe about life and write down the way these beliefs determine your direction. Form this into a statement of purpose, a creed for family living. Draw its definition from the love and imagination of the people who sail with you.

A Family Summary

On this page and the next, summarize your evaluation in this book of the members of your family.

DAD

Age:

Personality type (chapter 2):

Three outstanding character strengths (chap. 2):

Three main character weaknesses (chap. 2):

Love language (chap. 4):

Favorite home jobs (chap. 5):

Gifts and special abilities (chap. 6):

Dreams and ambitions (chap. 6):

Animal-type in conflict (chap. 8):

Favorite pastimes, hobbies (chap. 11):

Personal values (chap. 13):

MOM

Age:

Personality type (chapter 2):

Three outstanding character strengths (chap. 2):

Three main character weaknesses (chap. 2):

Love language (chap. 4):

Favorite home jobs (chap. 5):

Gifts and special abilities (chap. 6):

Dreams and ambitions (chap. 6):

Animal-type in conflict (chap. 8):

Favorite pastimes, hobbies (chap. 11):

Personal values (chap. 13):

name: _____

Age:

Personality type (chapter 2):

Three outstanding character strengths (chap. 2):

Three main character weaknesses (chap. 2):

Love language (chap. 4):

Favorite home jobs (chap. 5):

Gifts and special abilities (chap. 6):

Dreams and ambitions (chap. 6):

Animal-type in conflict (chap. 8):

Favorite pastimes, hobbies (chap. 11):

Personal values (chap. 13):

---

name: _____

Age:

Personality type (chapter 2):

Three outstanding character strengths (chap. 2):

Three main character weaknesses (chap. 2):

Love language (chap. 4):

Favorite home jobs (chap. 5):

Gifts and special abilities (chap. 6):

Dreams and ambitions (chap. 6):

Animal-type in conflict (chap. 8):

Favorite pastimes, hobbies (chap. 11):

Personal values (chap. 13):

---

name: _____   *age:*

Personality type (chapter 2):   Gifts and special abilities (chap. 6):

Three outstanding character strengths (chap. 2):   Dreams and ambitions (chap. 6):

Three main character weaknesses (chap. 2):   Animal-type in conflict (chap. 8):

Love language (chap. 4):   Favorite pastimes, hobbies (chap. 11):

Favorite home jobs (chap. 5):   Personal values (chap. 13):

About What You Believe

☞ What is the prevailing philosophy of your family? Check those that apply:
  ☐ We belong together no matter what happens; we are obligated to each other.
  ☐ We belong together as long as we feel good about being together.
  ☐ We are here to make the world a better place to live.
  ☐ We are here primarily for our own enjoyment.
  ☐ The best fun we have is the fun we make ourselves.
  ☐ Life owes us a living and we're out to make sure we get everything we deserve.

☞ Upon what ethics does your family base their behavior?
  ☐ It's okay if you don't get caught.   ☐ Honesty is the best policy.
  ☐ It's okay if you don't hurt anybody else.   ☐ To thine own self be true.
  ☐ If it feels good, it can't be wrong.   ☐ Do what's right with all your might.

☞ What are your spiritual beliefs?
  ☐ Human life is eternal and we are responsible to God for what we do.
  ☐ We are all gods and goddesses, and heaven and hell are played out on earth.
  ☐ Marriage is a sacrament and is meant to last a lifetime.
  ☐ Marriage is a commitment based on feelings of love and may be terminated when love for each other is no longer a reality.
  ☐ Our children should not be exposed to religious beliefs until they are old enough to make up their own minds.
  ☐ Our children should be taught spiritual principles as toddlers and brought up in our religious faith.

Your Family Creed

Formulate a statement of purpose or *family creed* detailing the vision you have for your family in the coming ten to twenty years. Include in this statement of purpose the unique perspective of your family. Detail the kinds of values that will guide you as you work toward fulfilling your purpose.

Simplify this statement in terms your children can understand, calling it a family motto, and place it where everyone can see it daily. (Notice the sample on the next page.)

Record a concise restatement of your family creed in the space shown.

Our Family Creed — A Sample

WE WILL LIVE TOGETHER, work together, and play together to enhance our sense of belonging to each other, and to enhance the self-esteem and confidence of each other. We will make home a place we like to be so that when we are away from it we have the support of knowing we are part of something bigger, and therefore can meet the world with courage and generosity.

Family Value 1: Family Harmony — a sense that "we belong together no matter what."

Priorities:
> A. Weekly time just for us, with no distractions.
> B. Strong, unique family traditions.
> C. Family project we start and complete together.
> D. Sensitive to and respectful of each other's feelings and opinions.

Family Value 2: Personal Growth and Creativity — our home is a place where our gifts are encouraged and enflamed.

Priorities:
> A. Exposure to music and fine art in our home.
> B. Availability of resources such as instruments, art supplies.
> C. Travel and field trips to concerts, museums and galleries.
> D. Praise and affirmation for creative initiatives.

Family Value 3: Moral Judgment — positive attitudes and character traits.

Priorities:
> A. Treating each other with gentleness and kindness.
> B. Respecting authority and the rights of others.
> C. Accepting the consequences of our actions.
> D. Requiring honesty with each other.

Family Value 4: Benevolence — a sense that "our family counts for others."

Priorities:
> A. Spending time with other families, other people.
> B. Exposure to other cultures and their needs.
> C. Participating in a family ministry project.
> D. Becoming sensitive to needs in our neighborhood.

Our Family Creed

Family Value 1:

Priorities:

Family Value 2:

Priorities:

Family Value 3:

Priorities:

Family Value 4:

Priorities:

Preparing for New Horizons

Setting Goals in Key Areas

Goal-oriented people take criticism and handle rejection better than those who have no goals. It is better to have a goal and not reach it, than to fail to set a goal at all.

LES CHRISTIE, *Getting a Grip on Time Management*

GENE BEDLEY SAYS, "It is through the process of attaining goals that new goals are envisioned." Goal achievement is more than the process of taking practical steps toward what you want to accomplish. It is a process of visualization, where new horizons are continually coming into view. The most successful families never really arrive because they find that new vistas and wide horizons keep them seeking and growing.

Goal setting is most effective when it is not just an occasional affair, but a way of life. It serves as psychological adrenalin for the person who knows where he wants to go, and knows that in the flow of getting there he may discover an uncharted tributary to the wide sea.

The following pages are designed so that you can put your family vision into a structure featuring...

Personal Goals :

- Career/Activities
- Emotional/ Psychological
- Social/Spiritual

Practical Goals :

- Family Time
- Homemaking
- Family Income

Interpersonal Goals :

- Our Marriage
- Between Parent & Child and Between Siblings
- Family Friendships

Each goal setting outline allows space to record…

- one *five-year goal* (the longer the planning period, the less detailed goals tend to be; the younger a child is, the shorter term his goals will be).
- one *one-year goal*.
- four *sub-goals* (providing detailed information about one-year goals).
- *action steps* (breaking the process into bite sized pieces).
- the *name of the person accountable* for each action step
- the *target date* for carrying each action step through to completion.

These last two steps are the most important. This is where most goal-setters drop the ball. Be sure each family member knows exactly what action step he is responsible for, and marks the target date on his personal calendar.

Finally, record…

- the *resources* necessary for successful completion of the action steps.
- the *name of the person responsible* for acquiring these resources.
- the *target date* for getting them.

Throughout this process proceed patiently, and involve every family member as much as possible.

Personal Goals — For Career and Activities

INSPIRATION

The moment of inspiration does not come to someone who lolls around expecting the gift to be free. It is no giveaway. It is the pearl for which we have to pay a great price, the price of intense loneliness, the price of that vulnerability which often allows us to be hurt; the less readily understandable price of hurting those we love. And I'm not sure it's a choice. If we're given a gift — and the size of the gift, great or small, is irrelevant — then most of us must serve it, like it or not. I say most of us, because I have seen people of great talent who have done nothing with it, and who mutter about getting down to work "when there's time."

For a woman who has chosen family as well as work, there's never time, and yet somehow time is given to us as time is given to the man who must sail a ship or chart the stars. A certain amount of stubbornness — pig-headedness — is essential.

MADELEINE L'ENGLE, *Walking on Water*

Work is love made visible. And if you cannot work with love but only with distaste, it is better that you should leave your work and sit at the gate of the temple and take alms of those who work with joy.

KAHLIL GIBRAN, *The Prophet*

FOLLOWING in this chapter is one blank goal-setting outline for career/activities goals for each family member.

Examples of five-year goals for parents:
- To obtain a Master's Degree in….
- To make my business financially stable.

Examples of five-year goals for kids:
- To develop daydreams into productive forms like stories, poems and paintings.
- To channel energy into activities that enhance our family life.

On the next page is sample information to be included in a goal-setting outline.

A Sample Outline for Career/Activities Goals

Name: Lea   Age: 9

I. **Five Year Goal:** To develop my daydreams into productive forms.

II. **One Year Goal:** To finish two short stories, illustrate them and submit them for publication to a children's journal or magazine.

Sub-goals:

A. *To choose from among the many stories I've started the two that have the most potential.*

Action steps:

   1. Put all stories in an orderly form like a notebook or scrapbook.
   2. Meet with Mom and Dad to discuss stories and choose two.

B. *To spend a half-hour three times a week working on my stories until they are finished.*

Action steps:

   1. Outline general story line.
   2. Decide on details of climax and conclusion.
   3. Discuss and edit with Mom and Dad.

C. *To spend a half-hour three times a week working on the illustrations until they are finished.*

Action steps:

   1. Choose medium (watercolor, color pencil, markers).
   2. Decide on how many illustrations.
   3. Outline themes of illustrations.

D. *To submit my two short stories for publication.*

Action steps:

   1. Research possibilities for publication and make list of names and addresses.
   2. Make clean copies of the stories
   3. Mail stories to publishers in order of where I most want to have them published.

III. **Resources Needed to Succeed**

   1. Loose leaf binder.
   2. Lined notebook paper/watercolor paper.
   3. Fine line automatic pencil.
   4. Colors in chosen medium.
   5. Envelopes and stamps.

goal-setting outline

Personal Goals — Career/Activities

Five-Year Goal:

One-Year Goal:

Subgoal #1:		
Action Steps:	Person Accountable:	Target Date:

Subgoal #2:		
Action Steps:	Person Accountable:	Target Date:

Subgoal #3:		
Action Steps:	Person Accountable:	Target Date:

Subgoal #4:		
Action Steps:	Person Accountable:	Target Date:

RESOURCES NEEDED:	Person Accountable:	Target Date:

Name: _____

goal-setting outline

Personal Goals — Career/Activities

Five-Year Goal:

One-Year Goal:

Subgoal #1:		
Action Steps:	Person Accountable:	Target Date:

Subgoal #2:		
Action Steps:	Person Accountable:	Target Date:

Subgoal #3:		
Action Steps:	Person Accountable:	Target Date:

Subgoal #4:		
Action Steps:	Person Accountable:	Target Date:

RESOURCES NEEDED:	Person Accountable:	Target Date:

Name: _____

goal-setting outline

Personal Goals — Career/Activities

Five-Year Goal:

One-Year Goal:

Subgoal #1:		
Action Steps:	Person Accountable:	Target Date:

Subgoal #2:		
Action Steps:	Person Accountable:	Target Date:

Subgoal #3:		
Action Steps:	Person Accountable:	Target Date:

Subgoal #4:		
Action Steps:	Person Accountable:	Target Date:

RESOURCES NEEDED:	Person Accountable:	Target Date:

Name: _____

goal-setting outline

Personal Goals — Career/Activities

Five-Year Goal:

One-Year Goal:

Subgoal #1:		
Action Steps:	Person Accountable:	Target Date:

Subgoal #2:		
Action Steps:	Person Accountable:	Target Date:

Subgoal #3:		
Action Steps:	Person Accountable:	Target Date:

Subgoal #4:		
Action Steps:	Person Accountable:	Target Date:

RESOURCES NEEDED:	Person Accountable:	Target Date:

Name: _____

goal-setting outline

Personal Goals — Career/Activities

Five-Year Goal:

One-Year Goal:

Subgoal #1:		
Action Steps:	Person Accountable:	Target Date:

Subgoal #2:		
Action Steps:	Person Accountable:	Target Date:

Subgoal #3:		
Action Steps:	Person Accountable:	Target Date:

Subgoal #4:		
Action Steps:	Person Accountable:	Target Date:

RESOURCES NEEDED:	Person Accountable:	Target Date:

Name: _____

Personal Goals — Emotional and Psychological

THE GIFT OF LONELINESS

Sometimes it seems as if we do everything possible to avoid the painful confrontation with our basic human loneliness, but perhaps the painful awareness of loneliness is an invitation to transcend our limitations and look beyond the boundaries of our existence. The awareness of loneliness might be a gift we must protect and guard,...filled with promise for him who can tolerate its sweet pain.

HENRI J. M. NOUWEN, *The Wounded Healer*

EXAMPLES of five-year emotional and psychological goals for parents:
- To stay healthy and available to the people I love.
- To confront my weakness in… and develop its twin strength.

Examples of five-year emotional and psychological goals for kids:
- To help… improve his relationship with authority figures, like teachers, parents, adult friends.
- To become more positive and optimistic in the way I look at things and respond to other people.

On the following pages you'll find an emotional/psychological goal-setting outline for each family member.

Personal Goals — Emotional/Psychological

Five-Year Goal:

One-Year Goal:

Subgoal #1:		
Action Steps:	Person Accountable:	Target Date:

Subgoal #2:		
Action Steps:	Person Accountable:	Target Date:

Subgoal #3:		
Action Steps:	Person Accountable:	Target Date:

Subgoal #4:		
Action Steps:	Person Accountable:	Target Date:

RESOURCES NEEDED:	Person Accountable:	Target Date:

Name: _____

goal-setting outline

Personal Goals — Emotional/Psychological

Five-Year Goal:

One-Year Goal:

Subgoal #1:		
Action Steps:	*Person Accountable:*	*Target Date:*

Subgoal #2:		
Action Steps:	*Person Accountable:*	*Target Date:*

Subgoal #3:		
Action Steps:	*Person Accountable:*	*Target Date:*

Subgoal #4:		
Action Steps:	*Person Accountable:*	*Target Date:*

RESOURCES NEEDED:		
	Person Accountable:	*Target Date:*

Name: _____

goal-setting outline

Personal Goals — Emotional/Psychological

Five-Year Goal:

One-Year Goal:

Subgoal #1:		
Action Steps:	Person Accountable:	Target Date:

Subgoal #2:		
Action Steps:	Person Accountable:	Target Date:

Subgoal #3:		
Action Steps:	Person Accountable:	Target Date:

Subgoal #4:		
Action Steps:	Person Accountable:	Target Date:

RESOURCES NEEDED:	Person Accountable:	Target Date:

Name: _____

goal-setting outline

Personal Goals — Emotional/Psychological

Five-Year Goal:

One-Year Goal:

Subgoal #1:		
Action Steps:	Person Accountable:	Target Date:

Subgoal #2:		
Action Steps:	Person Accountable:	Target Date:

Subgoal #3:		
Action Steps:	Person Accountable:	Target Date:

Subgoal #4:		
Action Steps:	Person Accountable:	Target Date:

RESOURCES NEEDED:	Person Accountable:	Target Date:

Name: _____

Personal Goals — Emotional/Psychological

Five-Year Goal:

One-Year Goal:

Subgoal #1:		
Action Steps:	Person Accountable:	Target Date:

Subgoal #2:		
Action Steps:	Person Accountable:	Target Date:

Subgoal #3:		
Action Steps:	Person Accountable:	Target Date:

Subgoal #4:		
Action Steps:	Person Accountable:	Target Date:

RESOURCES NEEDED:	Person Accountable:	Target Date:

Name: _____

Personal Goals — Social and Spiritual

US TWO

Wherever I am, there's always Pooh,

There's always Pooh and Me.

Whatever I do, he wants to do,

"Where are you going today?" says Pooh:

"Well, that's very odd 'cos I was too.

Let's go together," says Pooh, says he.

"Let's go together," says Pooh.

So wherever I am, there's always Pooh,

There's always Pooh and Me.

"What would I do?" I said to Pooh,

"If it wasn't for you," and Pooh said: "True,

It isn't much fun for One, but Two

Can stick together," says Pooh, says he.

"That's how it is," says Pooh.

A.A. MILNE, from *Now We Are Six*

EXAMPLES of five-year social or spiritual goals:

- To turn my acquaintances into friends.
- To create top quality friendships.
- To become more outgoing.
- To establish a foundation of knowledge for my spiritual beliefs.

Personal Goals — Social/Spiritual

Five-Year Goal:

One-Year Goal:

Subgoal #1:		
Action Steps:	Person Accountable:	Target Date:

Subgoal #2:		
Action Steps:	Person Accountable:	Target Date:

Subgoal #3:		
Action Steps:	Person Accountable:	Target Date:

Subgoal #4:		
Action Steps:	Person Accountable:	Target Date:

RESOURCES NEEDED:	Person Accountable:	Target Date:

Name: _____

goal-setting outline

Personal Goals — Social/Spiritual

Five-Year Goal:

One-Year Goal:

Subgoal #1:		
Action Steps:	*Person Accountable:*	*Target Date:*

Subgoal #2:		
Action Steps:	*Person Accountable:*	*Target Date:*

Subgoal #3:		
Action Steps:	*Person Accountable:*	*Target Date:*

Subgoal #4:		
Action Steps:	*Person Accountable:*	*Target Date:*

RESOURCES NEEDED:	*Person Accountable:*	*Target Date:*

Name: _____

goal-setting outline

Personal Goals — Social/Spiritual

Five-Year Goal:

One-Year Goal:

Subgoal #1:		
Action Steps:	Person Accountable:	Target Date:

Subgoal #2:		
Action Steps:	Person Accountable:	Target Date:

Subgoal #3:		
Action Steps:	Person Accountable:	Target Date:

Subgoal #4:		
Action Steps:	Person Accountable:	Target Date:

RESOURCES NEEDED:	Person Accountable:	Target Date:

Name: _____

goal-setting outline
Personal Goals — Social/Spiritual

Five-Year Goal:

Five-Year Goal:

Subgoal #1:		
Action Steps:	Person Accountable:	Target Date:

Subgoal #2:		
Action Steps:	Person Accountable:	Target Date:

Subgoal #3:		
Action Steps:	Person Accountable:	Target Date:

Subgoal #4:		
Action Steps:	Person Accountable:	Target Date:

RESOURCES NEEDED:	Person Accountable:	Target Date:

Name: _____

Personal Goals — Social/Spiritual

Five-Year Goal:

One-Year Goal:

Subgoal #1:		
Action Steps:	*Person Accountable:*	*Target Date:*

Subgoal #2:		
Action Steps:	*Person Accountable:*	*Target Date:*

Subgoal #3:		
Action Steps:	*Person Accountable:*	*Target Date:*

Subgoal #4:		
Action Steps:	*Person Accountable:*	*Target Date:*

RESOURCES NEEDED:	*Person Accountable:*	*Target Date:*

Name: _____

Practical Goals — Family Time

PEACE BEGINS AT HOME

Everybody today seems to be in such a terrible rush, anxious for greater developments and greater riches and so on, so that children have very little time for their parents. Parents have very little time for each other, and in the home begins the disruption of the peace of the world.

MOTHER TERESA, *A Gift from God*

> Prince, I warn you, under the rose,
> Time is the thief you cannot banish.
> These are my daughters, I suppose.
> But where in the world did the children vanish?

PHYLLIS MCGINLEY, *Ballade of Lost Objects*

Examples of five-year goals for family time:
- To learn to organize our time.
- To develop an attitude of giving family time priority.
- To create pockets of quality time with each other in great quantities
- To use our time for the good of others.

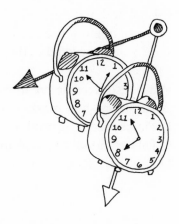

A Sample Outline for Family Time Goals

I. **Five-Year Goal:** To develop an attitude of giving family time priority so that every member of the family forms bonds with the other members of the family and so that we come to an understanding of how important we are to each other.

II. **One-Year Goal:** To develop a family hobby or project that all members enjoy and that will pull us together as a family; for example, to fix up and personalize our house.

Sub-goals:

A. To involve each family member in this project..

   Action Steps:

   1. Hold regular family meetings to talk about the project.
   2. Break tasks down into smallsteps and assign them to individuals.
   3. Attend a home trade fair as a family.
   4. Research magazines and cut out pictures of ideas for a scrapbook.

B. To have fun doing the project:

   Action Steps:

   1. On a weekly basis, give out small prizes and add stickers on a progress chart to recognize good work.
   2. Hold monthly patio parties to celebrate our progress.
   3. Enjoy great weekend snacks while we work.
   4. Work two by two, not alone.

C. To make a contribution to the beauty of the neighborhood.

   Action Steps:

   1. Paint the outside of the house.
   2. Plant flowers in flower boxes and rock gardens.

3. Design and make a family banner to hang out front.
4. Have an open-house garden party for the neighbors when the project is completed at the end of the year.

III. **What resources do we need to succeed?**

   A. Paint, brushes, masking tape and floor drapes.
   B. Flower seeds, topsoil, rocks.
   C. Fabric and sewing supplies for banner.
   D. Food, drink, and patio decorations.

Practical Goals — Family Time

Five-Year Goal:

One-Year Goal:

Subgoal #1:		
Action Steps:	Person Accountable:	Target Date:

Subgoal #2:		
Action Steps:	Person Accountable:	Target Date:

Subgoal #3:		
Action Steps:	Person Accountable:	Target Date:

Subgoal #4:		
Action Steps:	Person Accountable:	Target Date:

RESOURCES NEEDED:	Person Accountable:	Target Date:

Practical Goals — Homemaking

THE JOINT VENTURE

Because America's socioeconomic system has changed so much, men's roles have also been altered. Women's career climbing has established a consciousness of sexual equality among us. Women's demonstrated ability in the marketplace has altered the consciousness of the American people more than anything else. Young men, therefore, must learn to regard women as potential partners, not helpmates. This means clothes washing, food fixing, and sink scrubbing belong as much to husbands as to wives. Child raising, furthermore, is similarly a joint venture....

When children go off to school and — as is usually the case — mothers return to their careers, the sharing of domestic responsibilities by parents becomes even more important. Parents need to be available to receive their children home from school and to be involved in their extracurricular activities as well as religious education.

ANTHONY CAMPOLO, *Growing Up in America*

EXAMPLES of five-year goals for homemaking:

- To achieve a housekeeping routine where the workload is well distributed among all family members, and hassles and friction are minimized.
- To develop what it takes to maintain a clean, orderly home and a cheerful, upbeat spirit among us.
- To become more creative and colorful in our home (decorating, meals, housework routine, relationships).
- To get our garage and basement cleared out and cleaned up.

Practical Goals — Homemaking

Five-Year Goal:

One-Year Goal:

Subgoal #1:		
Action Steps:	*Person Accountable:*	*Target Date:*

Subgoal #2:		
Action Steps:	*Person Accountable:*	*Target Date:*

Subgoal #3:		
Action Steps:	*Person Accountable:*	*Target Date:*

Subgoal #4:		
Action Steps:	*Person Accountable:*	*Target Date:*

RESOURCES NEEDED:	*Person Accountable:*	*Target Date:*

Practical Goals — Family Income

ABOUT A MILLION DOLLARS SHORT

In my years of parenthood I've given a good deal of thought to the issue of children and money. I'm not speaking, here, of those depressing figures one encounters periodically, that tell what it costs to raise a child these days — figures that (if I'm to take them seriously) leave us, with our three kids, about a million dollars short. And that's not even counting where we'll stand if even one of them turns out to have an overbite.

What I'm speaking of is how a parent goes about teaching her children (as our Depression-educated parents used to put it) the value of a dollar. About money in general — what it is and where it comes from, where it goes, and most of all, the appropriate attitude with which to regard it. That you shouldn't love it, can't hate it. Have to respect it, mustn't worship it. Not to squander or hoard it. And really, this money-explaining business makes communicating the facts about sex or religion or the electoral college system seem pretty elementary.

JOYCE MAYNARD, *Domestic Affairs*

EXAMPLES of five-year goals for family income:

- To save enough money to make a down payment on a home.
- To establish a growing bank account for our children's education.
- To get completely out of debt and learn to live on our monthly income.
- To learn a new pattern of thinking; to anticipate what we can give away, not what we can get.

goal-setting outline
Practical Goals — Family Income

Five-Year Goal:

One-Year Goal:

Subgoal #1:		
Action Steps:	Person Accountable:	Target Date:

Subgoal #2:		
Action Steps:	Person Accountable:	Target Date:

Subgoal #3:		
Action Steps:	Person Accountable:	Target Date:

Subgoal #4:		
Action Steps:	Person Accountable:	Target Date:

RESOURCES NEEDED:	Person Accountable:	Target Date:

Interpersonal Goals — Our Marriage

THE SECOND WINE

When Christ stepped in at the wedding feast, what happened? The water was turned into wine, and the second wine was better than the first. There you have the most beautiful lesson about marriage: the second love in marriage is better than the first....

The second love is the important one. It is at this point that we love someone else instead of ourselves. It is a love which can put up with difficulties and defects, a love which is willing to accept suffering. This love summons all the resources within us and taxes every ounce of our strength. This is the love which makes adults out of us....

When Christ concocted a second batch of wine, everyone was amazed. You must communicate this same feeling of amazement to your children and those around you. If your children are not constantly amazed by your love for each other, if they are not in awe at the way your love grows, then you have not really taught them anything. If you do not teach them anything else, you must teach them that adulthood is a life worth living. You must stay alive and in love your whole life, or they will have no desire to grow up.

LOUIS EVELY, *Lovers in Marriage*

EXAMPLES of five-year goals for our marriage:

- To deepen our friendship.
- To perfect the art of conflict resolution.
- To enhance the romantic side of our marriage.
- To still be married.

A Sample Outline for Our Marriage Goals

I. Five-Year Goal: To perfect the art of conflict resolution.

II. One-Year Goal: To learn how to fight fairly.

Sub-goals:

A. To devise a plan of action when conflict arises between us.
   Action Steps:
   1. Meet and discuss what each of us would like the other to do when a conflict arises.
   2. Write it down, both sign it, then post it.
   3. Develop a code word or signal to remind us of our commitment during heated moments.

B. To educate ourselves about conflict resolution
   Action Steps:
   1. Read a book.
   2. Attend a marriage seminar.
   3. Talk to a counselor.

C. To find a way to learn from every conflict.
   Action Steps:
   1. Evaluate our reactions when we've cooled off.
   2. Make a journal of what we've learned about each other through conflict.
   3. Hold a state-of-the-marriage meeting every twomonths and ask ourselves, "How are we doing?"
   4. Reward ourselves with a romantic weekend every six months if we have followed our action steps.

III. What resources do we need to succeed?
   1. Book list on conflict resolution.
   2. Money for counselor and seminar.
   3. Patience.

goal-setting outline

His Goals for Our Marriage

Five-Year Goal:

Five-Year Goal:

Subgoal #1:		
Action Steps:	*Person Accountable:*	*Target Date:*

Subgoal #2:		
Action Steps:	*Person Accountable:*	*Target Date:*

Subgoal #3:		
Action Steps:	*Person Accountable:*	*Target Date:*

Subgoal #4:		
Action Steps:	*Person Accountable:*	*Target Date:*

RESOURCES NEEDED:	*Person Accountable:*	*Target Date:*

goal-setting outline

Her Goals for Our Marriage

Five-Year Goal:

Five-Year Goal:

Subgoal #1:		
Action Steps:	*Person Accountable:*	*Target Date:*

Subgoal #2:		
Action Steps:	*Person Accountable:*	*Target Date:*

Subgoal #3:		
Action Steps:	*Person Accountable:*	*Target Date:*

Subgoal #4.		
Action Steps:	*Person Accountable:*	*Target Date:*

RESOURCES NEEDED:	*Person Accountable:*	*Target Date:*

goal-setting outline

Our Goals Together for Our Marriage

Five-Year Goal:

Five-Year Goal:

Subgoal #1:		
Action Steps:	*Person Accountable:*	*Target Date:*

Subgoal #2:		
Action Steps:	*Person Accountable:*	*Target Date:*

Subgoal #3:		
Action Steps:	*Person Accountable:*	*Target Date:*

Subgoal #4:		
Action Steps:	*Person Accountable:*	*Target Date:*

RESOURCES NEEDED:	*Person Accountable:*	*Target Date:*

Interpersonal Goals —
Between Parent and Child, and Between Siblings

HUG'O WAR

I will not play at tug 'o war
I'd rather play at hug 'o war
Where everyone hugs instead of tugs
Where everyone tickles and rolls on the rug
Where everyone giggles and everyone grins
And everyone cuddles and everyone wins.

SHEL SILVERSTEIN, *Where The Sidewalk Ends*

EXAMPLES of five-year goals for relationships between parent and child:

- To accumulate wonderful memories of happy times with our children.
- To build trust and responsibility between ourselves and our children.
- To promote and enhance our children's sense of belonging to each other.
- To foster emotional attachment between our children through celebrations.

Examples of five-year goals for relationships between siblings:

- To build a caring attitude between us.
- To increase mutual respect and appreciation for each other.
- To argue less and get along better.

Dad's Goals for His Relationship with the Children

Five-Year Goal:

Five-Year Goal:

Subgoal #1:		
Action Steps:	Person Accountable:	Target Date:

Subgoal #2:		
Action Steps:	Person Accountable:	Target Date:

Subgoal #3:		
Action Steps:	Person Accountable:	Target Date:

Subgoal #4:		
Action Steps:	Person Accountable:	Target Date:

RESOURCES NEEDED:	Person Accountable:	Target Date:

Mom's Goals for Her Relationship with the Children

Five-Year Goal:

Five-Year Goal:

Subgoal #1:		
Action Steps:	Person Accountable:	Target Date:

Subgoal #2:		
Action Steps:	Person Accountable:	Target Date:

Subgoal #3:		
Action Steps:	Person Accountable:	Target Date:

Subgoal #4:		
Action Steps:	Person Accountable:	Target Date:

RESOURCES NEEDED:	Person Accountable:	Target Date:

Goals for My Sibling Relationships

Five-Year Goal:

Five-Year Goal:

Subgoal #1:		
Action Steps:	Person Accountable:	Target Date:

Subgoal #2:		
Action Steps:	Person Accountable:	Target Date:

Subgoal #3:		
Action Steps:	Person Accountable:	Target Date:

Subgoal #4:		
Action Steps:	Person Accountable:	Target Date:

RESOURCES NEEDED:	Person Accountable:	Target Date:

Name: _____

goal-setting outline

Goals for My Sibling Relationships

> Five-Year Goal:

> Five-Year Goal:

Subgoal #1:		
Action Steps:	*Person Accountable:*	*Target Date:*

Subgoal #2:		
Action Steps:	*Person Accountable:*	*Target Date:*

Subgoal #3:		
Action Steps:	*Person Accountable:*	*Target Date:*

Subgoal #4:		
Action Steps:	*Person Accountable:*	*Target Date:*

RESOURCES NEEDED:	*Person Accountable:*	*Target Date:*

Name: _____

goal-setting outline

Goals for My Sibling Relationships

Five-Year Goal:

Five-Year Goal:

Subgoal #1:		
Action Steps:	Person Accountable:	Target Date:

Subgoal #2:		
Action Steps:	Person Accountable:	Target Date:

Subgoal #3:		
Action Steps:	Person Accountable:	Target Date:

Subgoal #4:		
Action Steps:	Person Accountable:	Target Date:

RESOURCES NEEDED:	Person Accountable:	Target Date:

Name: _____

Interpersonal Goals — Family Friendships

Happy is the house that shelters a friend!

RALPH WALDO EMERSON

Examples of five-year goals for family friendships:

- To develop a relationship with our extended family through correspondence if they live in other cities.
- To become personal friends with at least one new family in our town each year for the next five years.
- To make grandparents the VIP's in our lives.
- To give a percentage of our time and money for the next five years to an organization that helps needy children in the Third World.

Our Goals for Family Friendships

Five-Year Goal:

Five-Year Goal:

Subgoal #1:		
Action Steps:	Person Accountable:	Target Date:

Subgoal #2:		
Action Steps:	Person Accountable:	Target Date:

Subgoal #3:		
Action Steps:	Person Accountable:	Target Date:

Subgoal #4:		
Action Steps:	Person Accountable:	Target Date:

RESOURCES NEEDED:	Person Accountable:	Target Date:

Our Goals — Family Friendships

One-Year Goal:

Five-Year Goal:

Subgoal #1:		
Action Steps:	Person Accountable:	Target Date:

Subgoal #2:		
Action Steps:	Person Accountable:	Target Date:

Subgoal #3:		
Action Steps:	Person Accountable:	Target Date:

Subgoal #4:		
Action Steps:	Person Accountable:	Target Date:

RESOURCES NEEDED:	Person Accountable:	Target Date:

Summary of Our One-Year Goals

Our Personal One-Year Goals:

Name:
Career/Activities goal:

Emotional/Psychological goal:

Social/Spiritual goal:

Name:
Career/Activities goal:

Emotional/Psychological goal:

Social/Spiritual goal:

Name:
Career/Activities goal:

Emotional/Psychological goal:

Social/Spiritual goal:

Name:
Career/Activities goal:

Emotional/Psychological goal:

Social/Spiritual goal:

Name:
Career/Activities goal:

Emotional/Psychological goal:

Social/Spiritual goal:

For each one of you, which goal will be your top priority this coming year?

Name:

Name:

Name:

Name:

Name:

Our Family One-Year Goals:

Family Time goal:

Homemaking goal:

Family Income goal:

Our Marriage goal (His):

Our Marriage goal (Hers):

Goal for Parent-Child Relationships (Dad):

Goal for Parent-Child Relationships (Mom):

Goal for Relationship between Siblings (1):

Goal for Relationship between Siblings (2):

Goal for Relationship between Siblings (3):

Family Friendships goal:

• Among your family goals, which will be your top priority this coming year?

Wrap Up

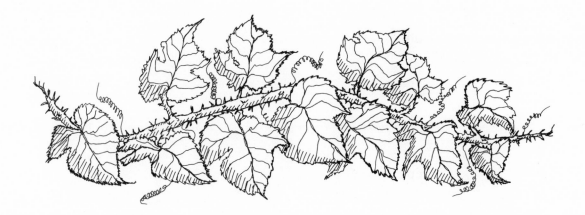

Updating the Process... Maintaining the Momentum

FAMILY LIFE PULLS MANY of us into a whirlpool of activity where outside pressures confront our values and consume our resources. Ben and I are finding that even a modest lifestyle requires hard work and long hours. Caught in the maelstrom, we fight to keep our heads above water, then struggle to get ahead, and we are sometimes distracted from homegrown values by what we *think* we want. Occasionally, we wonder what we're doing, where we're going, or whatever happened to the ideals of our youth.

In reality, the ideals are usually lying just below the surface. Some people are just more conscious of them than others. Some, who once wore flowers in their hair, sporting badges that said, "Make love, not war," now tote tots in mini vans with bumper stickers that say, "You can't hug children with nuclear arms." Others, who once experimented with marijuana, now want "Hugs, not drugs" for their teens.

Most people, like Ben and I, just want to have a small part in making the world a better place to live. We do that best by renewing our own vision within the sphere of the family. Our task demands the ability to stay organized and develop an overview of what lies ahead.

In updating the planning process and auditing our parenting skills, we want to ask ourselves new questions and listen to questions asked in indirect ways by our children.

• On the next page, take notes and write reflections on the feedback you've received from your family through this process.

• Also on the following page, list page numbers and chapter titles from *The Intimate Family* of those topics you would like to come back to.

• Schedule a date **six months** from now for reviewing with your family what you've accomplished. Write down that date in the space indicated on the next page, and circle it on your calendar as well.

When you review in six months, ask yourselves:

Notes...

Scheduled date for your SIX-MONTH review: _____

Scheduled date for your ONE-YEAR review: _____

* Is our family still motivated by our original vision?
* If our vision has changed, how should we modify our family creed?
* Do our family calendar and check-book registry over the last six months reflect agreement with the *values* we claim to believe in?
* If not, how do we need to modify our *priorities*?
* Have we gotten to know each other better through this process?
* What have we found out about *us* that we didn't know before we started?

• Schedule a date on the calendar **one year** from now to review each of the one-year goals you have already established. Ask yourselves:
* What went well in our steps toward each goal?
* What did we achieve in each area?
* Who worked to make it happen?
* What was key in making it work?
* What goals aren't yet fulfilled?
* How can we turn these into new goals?

At the end of one year, also discuss new developments in the family. Ask:
* What's bothering us? (What are our needs?)
* What do we want to see happen? (What are our dreams?)

* What plans will we make? (Set new goals, action steps, target dates.)

Strategic planning is not the final solution or the be-all-and-end-all answer to the crazy complexities of family life. There are occasions when the demands of raising a family become overwhelming. I sometimes lose the tender touch with my family. But real tenderness is, after all, a quality that is being produced in me by the very pressures I would so much like to avoid, as well as the situations that seem to raise more questions than answers.

I try to keep in mind something a poet wrote just for me, it seems:

> *Be patient toward all that is unsolved*
> *in your heart…*
> *And try to love*
> *the questions themselves…*
> *Do not seek the answers,*
> *which cannot be given*
> *because you would not be able*
> *to live them.*
> *And the point is,*
> *to live everything.*
> *Live the questions now.*
> *Perhaps you will then*
> *gradually,*
> *without noticing it,*
> *Live along some distant day*
> *into the answers.*

RAINER MARIA RILKE

Sources

Who We Are

PAGE:	REFERENCE:	SOURCE:
14	two relics	Russell Baker, *Growing Up* (New York: Congdon and Weed, Inc., 1982), p. 8.
26	rearing children	Phyllis Theroux, *Night Lights* (New York: Viking Penguin Inc., 1987), p. 30.
27	hyperactivity	Elaine K. McEwan, *Superkids?* (Elgin, Ill.: David C. Cook Publishing Co., 1988), p. 168.
28	tips for parenting	Kevin Leman, adapted from *The Birth Order Book* (New York: Dell Publishing Co., Inc., 1984), pp. 237-238, 269-270, 286-287.
32	personality preferences	Otto Kroeger and Janet M. Thuesen, *Type Talk* (New York: Delacorte Press, a division of The Bantam Doubleday Dell Publishing Group, Inc., 1988), pp. 13-21.
36	kid's temperaments	Stella Chess and Alexander Thomas, *Know Your Child* (New York: Basic Books, 1987) pp. 28-31.
40	character strengths	Joe White, *Orphans at Home* (Sisters, Ore.: Questar Publishers, Inc., 1988), pp. 170-173.
42-43	someday	Charles R. Swindoll, *Home: Where Life Makes Up It's Mind* (Portland, Ore.: Multnomah Press, 1979), pp.100-102.
44	cycle	John Powell, *The Secret of Staying in Love* (Niles, Ill.: Argus Communications, 1974), pp. 182-183.
45	milestones	Dennis and Barbara Rainey, adapted from *The Questions Book* (Sisters, Ore.: Questar Publishers, Inc., 1988), pp. 3, 6, 31.

Making the Most of Who We Are

PAGE:	REFERENCE:	SOURCE:
52	daring work	Merle Shain, *Courage My Love* (New York: Bantam Books, 1989), pp. 101, 105.
58	how important	Joy Mahaffey and Kathy Peel, adapted from *A Mother's Manual to Summertime Survival* (Pomona, Calif.: Focus on the Family Publishers, 1989), p. 71.
59	rate parents	Gene Bedley, adapted from "Hoover-Bedley Parent Perception Scale," *The Big R* (Irvine, Calif.: People-Wise Publications, 1985), pp. 67-70.
64	what is real	Margery Williams, *The Velveteen Rabbit* (New York: Random House, 1985) pp. 8-10.
67	adult stress	"Social Readjustment Rating Questionnaire," *Journal of Psychosomatic Research,* Volume 11, Table 1 (New York: Persamon Press, 1967), p. 214.
69	kids' stress	Tim Timmons, *Stress in the Family* (Eugene, Ore.: Harvest House Publishers, 1982), pp. 67-68.
71	prevent stress	E. E. Stephens, Jr., seminar material
72	twilight zone	Bill Cosby, *Love and Marriage* (New York: Doubleday, a division of Bantam Doubleday Dell Publishing Group, Inc. 1989), p.187.
73	catharsis	Erich Fromm, *The Art of Loving* (New York: Harper and Row Publishers, Inc., 1956), p. 86.
75	too much	Ralph E. Minear and William Proctor, *Kids Who Have Too Much* (Nashville: Thomas Nelson, Inc., 1989), pp. 19-20).
78	conflict style	Will Cunningham, *How to Enjoy a Family Fight* (Sisters, Ore.: Questar Publishers, Inc., 1988), pp. 151, 160, 167, 177, 178.
79	resolution	E. E. Stephens, Jr., seminar material
80	one approach	Stephens, seminar.

Making the Most of What We've Got

PAGE:	REFERENCE:	SOURCE:
82	never perfect	Mindy Bingham, Judy Edmondson, Sandy Stryker, *Choices* (Santa Barbara, Calif.: Advocacy Press, 1987), p. 168.
83	competitiveness	Dr. Benjamin Spock, "It's All Up to Us," *Newsweek,* Winter-Spring, 1990. p. 106.
85-86	financial	Don J. McMinn, *Strategic Living* (Grand Rapids, Mich.: Baker Book House Co., 1988).
88	college	(T. Rowe Price), Jane Bryant Quinn "Growing Old Frugally," *Newsweek,* Winter-Spring, 1990, p. 104.
90	retirement	(Ernst and Young), Quinn, "Growing Old Frugally," p. 103.
94	my rose	Antoine de Saint-Exupery, *The Little Prince* (New York: Harcourt Brace Jovanovich, 1943), pp. 70-71.
107	holidays	Marguerite Kelly and Elia Parsons, *The Mother's Almanac* (Garden City, N.Y.: Doubleday and Company, Inc., 1975), pp. 163-64.
116	time wasters	Edward R. Dayton, adapted from *Tools for Time Management* (Grand Rapids, Mich.: Zondervan)

Becoming More Than We'd Imagined

PAGE:	REFERENCE:	SOURCE:
120	wake up	Annie Dillard, *Teaching a Stone to Talk* (New York: Harper and Row, Publishers, Inc., 1982), pp. 97-98.
121	eye-opener	Louis Evely, *Lovers in Marriage* (Garden City N.Y.: Image Books, a division of Doubleday and Co., Inc., 1975), pp. 12, 17.
123	believe	Bobb Biehl, adapted from *Leadership Confidence* (Sisters, Ore.: Questar Publishers, Inc., 1988), p. 164.
128	courage	John Powell, *The Secret of Staying in Love* (Niles, Ill,: Argus Communications, 1974), p. 66.
134	dear dad	Joanna Cole and Stephanie Calmenson, *The Laugh Book* (New York: Doubleday, 1986).
135	creative	Patricia Ward and Martha Stout, *Christian Women at Work* (Grand Rapids, Mich.: Zondervan Publishing House), p. 108, 111.
135	childhood	Maurice Sendak, "Childhood: 'Brave, Mystical, Prosaic at the Same Time,'" *U.S. News and World Report,* March, 1986.
137	chalk dot	Roger Von Oech, *A Whack On the Side of the Head,* (New York: Warner Books, Inc., 1983), p. 22.
139-40	fun only	Dr. Abbie F. Salny, *The Mensa Book of Words, Word Games, Puzzles and Oddities* (New York, Harper and Row, Publishers, Inc., 1988).
140	button puzzles	Joanna Cole and Stephanie Calmenson, *The Laugh Book* (New York: Doubleday, 1986)

Renewing Our Purpose and Vision

PAGE:	REFERENCE:	SOURCE:
142	teach values	Paul Lewis, *40 Ways to Teach Your Child Value* (Wheaton, Ill.: Tyndale House Publishers, Inc., 1985), pp. 12-14.
143	twilight	Lee Iacocca, *Good Housekeeping,* November 1988.
144	values	Gail Sheehy, *Pathfinders* (New York: William Morrow and Company, Inc., 1981), p. 431.
146-48	kid's values	Mindy Bingham, Judy Edmondson, Sandy Stryker, *Choices,* (Santa Barbara, Ca.: Advocacy Press, 1987), p. 93.
150	sharing	Sheldon Vanauken, *A Severe Mercy* (New York: Harper and Row, Publishers, Inc., 1977), pp. 27, 29.
151	inspiration	Ben Alex, *Magic Moments in the Kingdom of Kids* (Nashville, Tenn.: Thomas Nelson Publishers, Inc., 1986), p. 52.
152	superparent	Mindy Bingham, Judy Edmondson, Sandy Stryker, *Choices* (Santa Barbara, Calif.: Advocacy Press, 1987), p. 169.
160	stars	Antoine de Saint-Exupery, *The Little Prince* (New York: Harcourt Brace Jovanovich, 1943), p. 85.

Preparing for New Horizons

PAGE: REFERENCE: SOURCE:

168   goal-oriented   Les Christie, *Getting a Grip on Time Management* (Wheaton, Ill.: Victor Books, 1984), p. 20.

170   stubbornness   Madeleine L'Engle, *Walking on Water* (Shaw Publications, 1980).

170   work   Kahlil Gibran, *The Prophet* (1923), in *Bartlett's Familiar Quotations* (USA: Little, Brown and Co., 1980).

177   loneliness   Henri J. M. Nouwen, *The Wounded Healer* (Garden City, New York, Doubleday and Company, Inc., 1972), p. 86.

183   us two   A.A. Milne, *Now We Are Six* (New York, Dell Publishing Co., Inc., by arrangement with E. P. Dutton and Co., Inc., 1927), pp. 35, 37.

189   rush   Mother Teresa, *A Gift for God* (San Francisco: Harper and Row Publishers, Inc., 1975), pp. 12-13.

189   prince   Phyllis McGinley, "Ballade of Lost Objects" (1954), in *Bartlett's Familiar Quotations* (USA: Little, Brown and Co., 1980).

192   men's roles   Anthony Campolo, *Growing Up in America* (Grand Rapids, Mich.: Youth Specialties Inc., Zondervan, 1989), p. 134.

194   million dollars   Joyce Maynard, *Domestic Affairs* (New York: Times Books, a division of Random House, Inc., 1987), pp. 93-94.

196   second wine   Louis Evely, *Lovers in Marriage* (Garden City, New York: Image Books, a division of Doubleday and Co., Inc., 1975), pp. 66-67.

201   hug o' war   Shel Silverstein, "Hug O' War," *Where the Sidewalk Ends* (New York: Harper and Row, Publishers, Inc., 1974), p. 19.

207   house   Ralph Waldo Emerson, "Friendship," *Essays, First Series* (1841), *The Harper Book of American Quotations* (New York: Carruth and Ehrlich Books, Inc. 1988) p. 109.

Wrap Up

217   questions   Rainer Maria Rilke, *Letters to a Young Poet,* translation by M.D. Herter Norton (W. W. Norton and Company, Inc., 1934).

Family Records
and Directories

Dad's full name _____

Date of birth:

Place of birth:

Social Security number:

Passport number:

Passport expiration date:

Driver's license number:

Personal records and documents are located:

Occupation:

Business name:

Business address:

Business telephone number:

Business hours:

Best time to call:

Employer/Supervisor's name:

Persons to contact in case of emergency—

Closest neighbors:

Closest relatives:

Best friends:

Dad's medical information

Height:

Weight:

Medical limitations, restrictions:

Regular medications:

Medical doctor(s):

—address and phone:

Emergency facility:

Medical insurance carrier/agent:

Medical insurance group or policy number:

Filing procedures for insurance claims:

Medical records are located:

Medical advice:

Mom's full name _____

Date of birth:

Place of birth:

Social Security number:

Passport number:

Passport expiration date:

Driver's license number:

Personal records and documents are located:

Occupation:

Business name:

Business address:

Business telephone number:

Business hours:

Best time to call:

Employer/Supervisor's name:

Persons to contact in case of emergency—

Closest neighbors:

Closest relatives:

Best friends:

Mom's medical information

Height:

Weight:

Medical limitations, restrictions:

Regular medications:

Medical doctor(s):

—address and phone:

Emergency facility:

Medical insurance carrier/agent:

Medical insurance group or policy number:

Filing procedures for insurance claims:

Medical records are located:

Medical advice:

Child's full name _____

Date of birth:

Place of birth:

Social Security number:

Passport number:

Passport expiration date:

Driver's license number:

Personal records and documents are located:

School:

School address:

School telephone number:

Teachers' full names:

Principal's name:

Principal's secretary's name:

Part-time employer's name:

Part-time work address:

Part-time work telephone number:

Best friends:

Medical information for _____
NAME

Height:

Weight:

Medical limitations, restrictions:

Regular medications:

Medical doctor(s):

—address and phone:

School physician or nurse:

Emergency facility:

Medical insurance information:

Medical records are located:

Medical advice:

Child's full name _____

Date of birth:

Place of birth:

Social Security number:

Passport number:

Passport expiration date:

Driver's license number:

Personal records and documents are located:

School:

School address:

School telephone number:

Teachers' full names:

Principal's name:

Principal's secretary's name:

Part-time employer's name:

Part-time work address:

Part-time work telephone number:

Best friends:

Medical information for _____

Height:

Weight:

Medical limitations, restrictions:

Regular medications:

Medical doctor(s):

—address and phone:

School physician or nurse:

Emergency facility:

Medical insurance information:

Medical records are located:

Medical advice:

Child's full name _____

Date of birth:

Place of birth:

Social Security number:

Passport number:

Passport expiration date:

Driver's license number:

Personal records and documents are located:

School:

School address:

School telephone number:

Teachers' full names:

Principal's name:

Principal's secretary's name:

Part-time employer's name:

Part-time work address:

Part-time work telephone number:

Best friends:

Medical information for _____

Height:

Weight:

Medical limitations, restrictions:

Regular medications:

Medical doctor(s):

—address and phone:

School physician or nurse:

Emergency facility:

Medical insurance information:

Medical records are located:

Medical advice:

Other Professionals

Family dentist:

—address and phone:

Dental insurance information:

Marriage and family counselor:

—address and phone:

Attorney/estate executor:

—address and phone:

Family will or trust record numbers/dates:

Documents are located:

Children's authorized guardian in event of parents' death:

Insurance

Life and/or disability insurance company/agent:

—address and telephone:

Policy dates, types, amounts of coverage, and numbers:

Policies are located:

Automobile/home insurance carrier/agent:

—address and telephone:

Policy numbers:

Auto (1) model/ID number:

Auto (1) license number/expiration date:

Auto (2) model/ID number:

Auto (2) license number/expiration date:

Documents are located:

Information on other vehicles:

Financial

Bank or credit union (1):

—address and phone:

Savings account number:

Checking account number:

Safe deposit box number:

Name of bank manager/loan officer:

Bank or credit union (2):

—address and phone:

Savings account number:

Checking account number:

Safe deposit box number:

Name of bank manager/loan officer:

Passports, credit card records are located:

Accountant:

—address and telephone:

Tax records are located:

Financial

Investments and estate/financial adviser:

—address and phone:

stocks and/or bonds, savings and certificates, tax-deferred plans, mutual funds:

amount, record numbers:

documents are located:

home deed number:

home loan number/date to be paid off:

other outstanding loans (with account numbers):

documents are located:

Service/Support/Community Involvement

Professional organizations we belong to (with addresses and phone numbers):

Church/synagogue:
—address and phone:

Name of priest/pastor/rabbi:
Office and home phone:

Clubs (with contact persons and phone numbers):

Committees (with contact persons and phone numbers):

Support groups (with contact persons and phone numbers):

Charities (with contact persons and phone numbers):

Boards, advisory councils:

Neighborhood association:

Our Children's Friends and Pen Pals

names, addresses, and telephone numbers

_____

_____

_____

_____

_____

_____

_____

_____

_____

_____

_____

_____

_____

_____

_____

_____

_____

Birthday/Anniversary Card List

january

february

march

april

may

june

Birthday/Anniversary Card List

july

august

september

october

november

december

friends & relatives

name _____ birthday _____

name _____ birthday _____

children's names & birthdays _____

home address _____

_____ telephone _____

personal interests (ideas for gifts) _____

---

name _____ birthday _____

name _____ birthday _____

children's names & birthdays _____

home address _____

_____ telephone _____

personal interests (ideas for gifts) _____

---

name _____ birthday _____

name _____ birthday _____

children's names & birthdays _____

home address _____

_____ telephone _____

personal interests (ideas for gifts) _____

---

name _____ birthday _____

name _____ birthday _____

children's names & birthdays _____

home address _____

_____ telephone _____

personal interests (ideas for gifts) _____

---

name _____ birthday _____

name _____ birthday _____

children's names & birthdays _____

home address _____

_____ telephone _____

personal interests (ideas for gifts) _____

friends & relatives

name _____ birthday _____

name _____ birthday _____

children's names & birthdays _____

home address _____

_____ telephone _____

personal interests (ideas for gifts) _____

name _____ birthday _____

name _____ birthday _____

children's names & birthdays _____

home address _____

_____ telephone _____

personal interests (ideas for gifts) _____

name _____ birthday _____

name _____ birthday _____

children's names & birthdays _____

home address _____

_____ telephone _____

personal interests (ideas for gifts) _____

name _____ birthday _____

name _____ birthday _____

children's names & birthdays _____

home address _____

_____ telephone _____

personal interests (ideas for gifts) _____

name _____ birthday _____

name _____ birthday _____

children's names & birthdays _____

home address _____

_____ telephone _____

personal interests (ideas for gifts) _____

friends & relatives

name _____   birthday _____
name _____   birthday _____
children's names & birthdays _____
home address _____
_____   telephone _____
personal interests (ideas for gifts) _____

name _____   birthday _____
name _____   birthday _____
children's names & birthdays _____
home address _____
_____   telephone _____
personal interests (ideas for gifts) _____

name _____   birthday _____
name _____   birthday _____
children's names & birthdays _____
home address _____
_____   telephone _____
personal interests (ideas for gifts) _____

name _____   birthday _____
name _____   birthday _____
children's names & birthdays _____
home address _____
_____   telephone _____
personal interests (ideas for gifts) _____

name _____   birthday _____
name _____   birthday _____
children's names & birthdays _____
home address _____
_____   telephone _____
personal interests (ideas for gifts) _____

friends & relatives

name _____ birthday _____
name _____ birthday _____
children's names & birthdays _____
home address _____
_____ telephone _____
personal interests (ideas for gifts) _____

name _____ birthday _____
name _____ birthday _____
children's names & birthdays _____
home address _____
_____ telephone _____
personal interests (ideas for gifts) _____

name _____ birthday _____
name _____ birthday _____
children's names & birthdays _____
home address _____
_____ telephone _____
personal interests (ideas for gifts) _____

name _____ birthday _____
name _____ birthday _____
children's names & birthdays _____
home address _____
_____ telephone _____
personal interests (ideas for gifts) _____

name _____ birthday _____
name _____ birthday _____
children's names & birthdays _____
home address _____
_____ telephone _____
personal interests (ideas for gifts) _____

friends & relatives

name _____ birthday _____
name _____ birthday _____
children's names & birthdays _____
home address _____
_____ telephone _____
personal interests (ideas for gifts) _____

name _____ birthday _____
name _____ birthday _____
children's names & birthdays _____
home address _____
_____ telephone _____
personal interests (ideas for gifts) _____

name _____ birthday _____
name _____ birthday _____
children's names & birthdays _____
home address _____
_____ telephone _____
personal interests (ideas for gifts) _____

name _____ birthday _____
name _____ birthday _____
children's names & birthdays _____
home address _____
_____ telephone _____
personal interests (ideas for gifts) _____

name _____ birthday _____
name _____ birthday _____
children's names & birthdays _____
home address _____
_____ telephone _____
personal interests (ideas for gifts) _____

friends & relatives

name _____ birthday _____

name _____ birthday _____

children's names & birthdays _____

home address _____

_____ telephone _____

personal interests (ideas for gifts) _____

---

name _____ birthday _____

name _____ birthday _____

children's names & birthdays _____

home address _____

_____ telephone _____

personal interests (ideas for gifts) _____

---

name _____ birthday _____

name _____ birthday _____

children's names & birthdays _____

home address _____

_____ telephone _____

personal interests (ideas for gifts) _____

---

name _____ birthday _____

name _____ birthday _____

children's names & birthdays _____

home address _____

_____ telephone _____

personal interests (ideas for gifts) _____

---

name _____ birthday _____

name _____ birthday _____

children's names & birthdays _____

home address _____

_____ telephone _____

personal interests (ideas for gifts) _____

friends & relatives

name _____ birthday _____
name _____ birthday _____
children's names & birthdays _____
home address _____
_____ telephone _____
personal interests (ideas for gifts) _____

name _____ birthday _____
name _____ birthday _____
children's names & birthdays _____
home address _____
_____ telephone _____
personal interests (ideas for gifts) _____

name _____ birthday _____
name _____ birthday _____
children's names & birthdays _____
home address _____
_____ telephone _____
personal interests (ideas for gifts) _____

name _____ birthday _____
name _____ birthday _____
children's names & birthdays _____
home address _____
_____ telephone _____
personal interests (ideas for gifts) _____

name _____ birthday _____
name _____ birthday _____
children's names & birthdays _____
home address _____
_____ telephone _____
personal interests (ideas for gifts) _____

friends & relatives

name _____ birthday _____
name _____ birthday _____
children's names & birthdays _____
home address _____
_____ telephone _____
personal interests (ideas for gifts) _____

name _____ birthday _____
name _____ birthday _____
children's names & birthdays _____
home address _____
_____ telephone _____
personal interests (ideas for gifts) _____

name _____ birthday _____
name _____ birthday _____
children's names & birthdays _____
home address _____
_____ telephone _____
personal interests (ideas for gifts) _____

name _____ birthday _____
name _____ birthday _____
children's names & birthdays _____
home address _____
_____ telephone _____
personal interests (ideas for gifts) _____

name _____ birthday _____
name _____ birthday _____
children's names & birthdays _____
home address _____
_____ telephone _____
personal interests (ideas for gifts) _____

PARENTING IDEA BANK
New Resources, Things to Try, etc.

Scrapbook of Sayings

our kids' cute expressions

_____

_____

_____

_____

_____

_____

_____

_____

_____

_____

_____

_____

_____

_____

_____

_____

_____

_____

Answers to FOR FUN ONLY, pages 139-40:

1. SIX (Curve the first line, leave the second as is, and cross the last two.)

3. Friday

5. flower (the only one that is not an artistic work made by man)

6. radish (both potatoes and radishes grow in the ground)

7. *First button puzzle:* Take the end pennies on the bottom row, and place them on either end of the second row. Then take the top penny and put it at the bottom.

    Second button puzzle: Pick up the bottom penny and set it on top of the middle one.

8. 9 P.M.

9. 11, and 5. (Alternate numbers go up by 2 and down by 1, starting with 1 and 10.)

10. BANANA